The Authors

LEO W. SIMMONS, Ph.D. Professor of sociology, Yale University. Formerly visiting professor of anthropology, Cornell University Medical College.

HAROLD G. WOLFF, M.D. Professor of medicine (neurology), Cornell University Medical College, and attending physician at New York Hospital, New York, N. Y.

STATEMENT CONCERNING PUBLICATIONS OF RUSSELL SAGE FOUNDATION

Russell Sage Foundation was established in 1907 by Mrs. Russell Sage "for the improvement of social and living conditions in the United States of America." While the general responsibility for management of the Foundation is vested in the Board of Trustees, the responsibility for facts, conclusions, and interpretations in its publications rests with the authors and not upon the Foundation, its Trustees, or its staff. Publication under the imprint of the Foundation does not imply agreement by the organization with all opinions or interpretations expressed. It does imply that care has been taken that the work on which a manuscript is based has been thoroughly done.

SOCIAL SCIENCE IN MEDICINE

By

LEO W. SIMMONS
Professor of Sociology, Yale University

HAROLD G. WOLFF
Professor of Medicine (Neurology)
Cornell University Medical College

RUSSELL SAGE FOUNDATION
New York ~ ~ *1954*

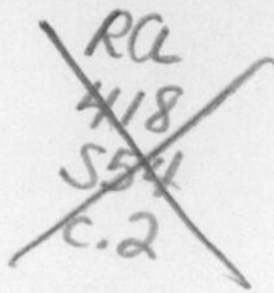

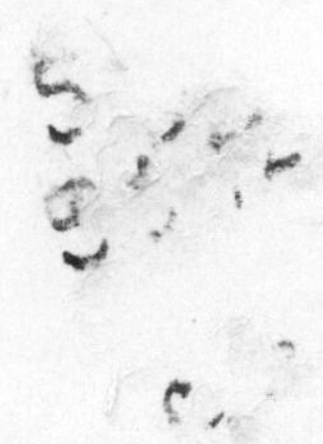

Printed in the United States
of America

Library of Congress
Catalog Card Number: 54-9401

WM. F. FELL CO., PRINTERS
PHILADELPHIA, PA.

Contents

Foreword

In 1949 RUSSELL SAGE FOUNDATION announced its current program for the improvement of the utilization of research in the social sciences in professional practice. It was intended that this program would be carried on in collaboration with many of the professions, particularly those most directly concerned with social welfare. The immediate response of the medical profession, which has resulted in the initiation of a greater number of Foundation projects in the field of the health services than in any other, was not anticipated but it was welcomed. Medical leaders concerned about social and psychological aspects of health were unexpectedly eager for increased collaboration with social scientists.

Yet medical science generally is regarded, at least by ordinary laymen, as having to do almost exclusively with research of a physical or biological nature. Every schoolboy who thinks of becoming a physician has it quickly impressed on him that he must be proficient in chemistry and biology, and perhaps in other branches of natural science as well. Patients know that the medicines administered to them are chemicals and that the technical equipment of hospital and private office has been made possible by advances in physics, chemistry, and biology. They take for granted that the skills of the physician are largely the product of knowledge gained from the natural sciences. This popular view of modern medicine as predominantly biophysical accurately reflects the overwhelming dependence of current practice on the natural sciences; it leaves out of account or minimizes the psychosocial factors in illness and health.

The medical profession never has been unmindful of social environment and personal traits as elements in sickness. Even the word "psychosomatic" is well over a century in age, and the approach to the problems of health which it represents is as old as medical practice itself. Until recently, however, the related disciplines of sociology, social psychology, and social anthropology have been inadequate in concept, research method, and substantive content for purposes of medical research and practice. As Dr. Leo W. Simmons and Dr. Harold G. Wolff so ably demonstrate in the following pages, these disciplines now have advanced to a point where fruitful collaboration between medical and social scientists is feasible and well in process of development.

The success of such collaboration is dependent on a degree of interprofessional understanding which so far has been achieved by few individuals in either social research or medicine. One problem has been the difficulty of bringing into orderly relationship within an eclectic theoretical structure the numerous and complicated separate pieces of medically useful social science knowledge and the even vaster number of medical questions to which social research may be expected to make a contribution. A second problem has been the scarcity of persons well trained in the social sciences and also sufficiently familiar with some segment of the medical field to be able to use their research knowledge and skills effectively. The collaborating social scientist must know the substantive area of collaboration, not merely his own discipline. It is understandable that few people have prepared themselves for careers in a nebulous interprofessional field that requires detailed and easy familiarity with two professional ways of working and living.

Dr. Simmons and Dr. Wolff offer a framework for collaboration between social science and medicine that will aid in relating to each other many seemingly fragmentary and independent studies of medical significance. Their work will also be an encouragement and guide to others in the frontier area of medicine and social research.

DONALD YOUNG
General Director
Russell Sage Foundation

May 10, 1954

Preface

DURING THE PAST HALF-CENTURY in our clinics and laboratories the medical arts have been integrated with the biological and physical sciences to the great benefit of mankind.[1] This fusion of art and science has pushed medical knowledge to the point where persons doing research are aware that human beings should be studied in their day-to-day environments as well as in the laboratory and the clinic, and in psychosocial as well as biophysical perspective, if we are to understand fully the conditions and processes of both health and disease.

Medical leadership is thus turning inquiringly to the social sciences for help in solving some of its problems. The social scientists are responding to the best of their ability, but their training has been so different from that of the medical specialists that comprehension of the issues under investigation has been impeded by lack of communication between the two groups. This inability to communicate in common professional language has often been aggravated by differences in concepts, methods, and techniques.[2] In spite of such handicaps, social scientists are being called upon in increasing numbers to fill positions on interdisciplinary research teams.[3]

For the purpose of studying opportunities for closer participation between personnel in the social science and medical fields, an exploratory project, sponsored by Russell Sage Foundation, was initiated two years ago at the New York

[1] See Shryock, R. H., "The Historian Looks at Medicine," 1937; Idem, *The Development of Modern Medicine*, 1947; Sigerist, H. E., *Man and Medicine*, 1932.

The reader will find in the Bibliography of this volume full information concerning names of publishers, place of publication, and so on, for all writings cited in the footnotes.

[2] Caudill, William, and B. H. Roberts, "Pitfalls in the Organization of Interdisciplinary Research," 1951.

[3] Statement formulated in collaboration with members of Committee on Social Science and Medicine at Yale University.

Hospital-Cornell Medical Center under the leadership of the senior author of this volume. There have been two results of this undertaking in medical-social collaboration. In the first place, four special studies were launched: (1) an examination of the physician-patient relationship over extended periods of therapy; (2) the analysis of interpersonal relationships in an experimental program of nursing consultation service; (3) a survey study of problems and procedures in night nursing; and (4) a case study of fifty families who have made very extensive use of the medical services of the New York Hospital and its clinics. Reports of these studies are in preparation.

The second result is the present volume, which explores some of the major areas of interest shared by medicine and social science. Particular reference is made to those concepts and formulations that bear directly upon the problems of health and that may forward collaborative research.

The book is addressed primarily to students in medicine and the social sciences interested in training for research in these related areas. It is the hope of the authors that the report may also interest public-spirited citizens who share responsibility for health and welfare programs, and that it may be of some value to the members of several professional groups, such as medical administrators, educators, public health officials, social workers, and nurses who are closely allied with our medical specialists in the prevention and treatment of disease.

We are deeply indebted to Carolyn Zeleny and Edmund H. Volkart for their part in making possible the present publication. Dr. Zeleny collaborated in the initial analysis of data and in preparing the early drafts of the manuscript. Professor Volkart assisted in the final revision of the book. Dr. Stanhope Bayne-Jones has been a constant source of inspiration and support for the exploratory project. Thanks are due to David P. Barr for encouragement and help throughout the study and to Virginia Dunbar and Joseph C. Hinsey for their reading of the manuscript.

LEO W. SIMMONS, Ph.D.

May 10, 1954 HAROLD G. WOLFF, M.D.

Social Science in Medicine

CHAPTER 1

Medicine and Social Science

During the greater part of the twentieth century, "scientific medicine," as outlined more than forty years ago by the Flexner Report,[1] has been the chief medical goal and specialization its dominant pattern. This same period has seen the development of the hospital as the chief treatment and research institution, exemplifying in its depersonalized and fractionated services, as well as its refined procedures, the ideals and principles of the scientific approach to the problem of disease. Although these emphases still largely prevail, there are signs that a new era is opening in which medical care will be conceived in broader terms.[2] Advances made in public health, psychiatry, psychoanalysis, social work, and social science have given rise to a new concept of comprehensive (in contrast to specialized) medical care, which is modifying the former definitions and objectives of scientific medicine.

Comprehensive care has become a popular slogan, both as applied to preventive medicine, on a community or wider basis, and to patient care within the hospital. In the era that lies ahead, leaders believe, this new outlook will win more general acceptance and will gradually become more effectively coordinated with the earlier approach. This will entail "some reconciliation between what has been called scientific medicine and what is now called comprehensive medicine, some better

[1] Flexner, Abraham, *Medical Education in the United States and Canada*, 1910.

[2] See the following articles, published in 1950: Barr, D. P., "The Changing Order in Medicine"; Bayne-Jones, Stanhope, "The Hospital as a Center of Preventive Medicine"; Johnson, W. M., "The Training of a General Practitioner"; Long, P. H., "A Future for Preventive Medicine"; Moore, R. A., "The Physician and the Law"; O'Hara, Dwight, "Today's Trends in Medical Education"; Rappleye, W. C., "The Physician in Modern Society"; White, P. D., "La Médecine du Coeur." For further discussion and references see p. 48.

adjustment of the specialist to the generalist, and some restructuring of both medical education and medical care to fit the needs of a more knowledgeable social order."[1]

The recognition of sociological factors as intervening variables in disease is, of course, nothing new for medicine either in its primitive backgrounds or its historical developments.[2] Indeed, the emotional, attitudinal, and interpersonal components of disease are rarely ever denied by physicians as significant factors in health, although in practice they may often be neglected. Some tacit recognition of the relevance of social dynamics to disease has generally been granted by the medical profession even at those points where it has shown diffidence or incapacity to deal with them constructively.

It is easy to surmise that the great therapists, past and present, have exercised remarkable talents in the treatment of patients as people responding to complex social pressures. The success of these therapists has rested on a psychosocial base as well as a biophysical one. In their practice they have been able to combine sound principles from both spheres in a gifted, if largely intuitive manner. At this stage of our knowledge, however, a haphazard approach is no longer adequate, for it leaves to chance insight many things that are already partially understood and formulated.

[1] *Thirty-fourth Annual Report of the Commonwealth Fund*, 1952, p. 2.

Other recent Commonwealth Fund publications that have called attention to the changes going on in medicine are the following:

Allen, R. B., *Medical Education and the Changing Order*, 1946; Idem, *Medicine in the Changing Order*, 1947; Ashford, Mahlon, editor, *Trends in Medical Education*, 1949; Curran, J. A., and Eleanor Cockerill, *Widening Horizons in Medical Education*, 1948; Robinson, G. C., *The Patient as a Person*, 1939; Shryock, R. H., *American Medical Research, Past and Present*, 1947; Stern, B. J., *American Medical Practice in the Perspectives of a Century*, 1945; Stieglitz, E. J., *A Future for Preventive Medicine*, 1945.

See also the following articles: Grant, J. B., "Toward Health: Certain Trends," 1946; Gregg, Alan, "The Future of Medicine," 1937; Leavell, H. R., "New Occasions Teach New Duties," 1953; Meleney, H. E., "The Next Ten Years in Medicine," 1947; *Idem*, "Preventive Medical Services for the Family," 1949; *Idem*, "Preventive Medicine in Tomorrow's World," 1950; Pemberton, John, "Possible Developments in Social Medicine," 1943.

[2] Shryock, R. H., *The Development of Modern Medicine*, 1947; Sigerist, H. E., *A History of Medicine*, 1951, vol. 1; Zilboorg, Gregory, and G. W. Henry, *A History of Medical Psychology*, 1941; Zilboorg, Gregory, *Mind, Medicine, and Man*, 1943.

It can now be taken for granted, for instance, that for optimum medical success it is essential to reduce biological phenomena to scientific formulation. This same principle should apply with equal force to personal and social phenomena. It is entirely untenable, moreover, to assume that medical progress in the physical sciences renders social science less essential, or even less useful, in medical practice. The claim that in earlier times practitioners were forced to consider and treat their patients as persons and members of society in order to achieve any substantial success because their biophysical knowledge was inadequate, provides dubious justification for the neglect of social components in modern medical practice. The obvious challenge to the medical man of the present and the future, it would seem, is to develop in a systematic and scientific way and to utilize so far as possible the relevant principles and skills in both fields of forces.

In a broad medical program, and not infrequently in the treatment of a single patient, the choice of either sphere in the dynamics of disease, with neglect of the other, sets up a false dichotomy and inspires a half-handed and patchwork policy in medical care for which the recipients of the service may pay with compromises in their health. Even excellent medical care on strictly physical and depersonalized grounds is not good enough to meet human needs, public demands, or the ideals of our leading therapists if something superior is possible on a more balanced and comprehensive basis. Although there is no wish to minimize here the primary importance of the physical factors involved in illness, a sound foundation clearly must include whatever the social sciences can contribute to the personal and more comprehensive problems of medical care.[1]

Integration of the social disciplines with medicine, however, has necessarily been slow to evolve. The behavioral sciences

[1] Hinsie, L. E., *The Person in the Body*, 1945; Ryle, J. A., "Social Medicine," 1944; Stallybrass, C. O., "Social Medicine and the Comprehensive Medical Service," 1944.

were established late and they have required a long period of incubation and growth before the findings from various branches could be fitted into a consistent and meaningful pattern of knowledge.

Even then, the practical value of social scientific concepts and skills did not enlist immediate medical interest. It was probably the social worker, with her knack and skill in dealing with concrete personal problems in social context, who first attracted the attention of the physician because of her ability to place at his disposal much of the useful social data which the earlier "family doctor" had been able to gather firsthand in his routine medical practice. She became the physician's first professional ally from the social field.[1] However, her opportunities, functions, and particularly her scientific scope were limited. Without much systematic training in research methods or concepts, and overburdened with case schedules and service activities, she was unable alone to represent to medicine the progress made in the various branches of the rapidly expanding social sciences.

Indeed, for a time the interests of the social workers turned more directly to psychology, and especially to psychoanalysis, for concepts and principles that would relate and interpret their findings concerning the patient and his family or other intimate group memberships. In terms of the dynamics involved, the problems of the individual were viewed primarily from the personal side. For the use of the social worker, the recognition and partial clarification of the role of unconscious motivations and interpersonal conflicts held great promise, particularly as applied to the early and intimate relationships of family life.

In different context and with varied emphases, other useful concepts have been emerging in the behavioral sciences that clarify the function of the social and cultural dynamics which impinge directly upon and largely determine human adapta-

[1] Bruno, F. J., *Trends in Social Work*, 1948.

tions.[1] Many of these background factors of the social environment, which channel and determine individual and group behavior, are recognized, like those interesting the psychoanalyst, as being mainly indeliberate and automatic in their effect and for that reason especially well suited to study on an objective basis.

The social sciences that study these factors, however, were separately established, with widely divergent types of orientation. For some time they continued to pursue relatively independent courses, developing their own concepts and setting up their own frames of reference. More recently, however, the lines of thought and types of research in the several fields have been converging, with a consequent merging and reinforcing of the formulations of psychological and social dynamics in personal and group adaptations. A natural next step is to relate psychosocial formulations to findings in the biophysical field, both conceptually and with practical intent. Some tentative efforts have already encouraged the pulling down o fences between the different behavioral sciences and some joining of hands with the physical sciences all along the line.

It is perhaps in the study of the personal and social components of illness that the integration of psychosocial and biophysical theories around the problems of the individual is offered the greatest practical challenge. Here the varied approaches for both research and application are brought into alignment to provide a broader basis for diagnosis and a more comprehensive foundation for programs of prevention, therapy, and rehabilitation.

Medicine is, indeed, in a strategic position for the integration of biological and sociological knowledge. In the ranks of the professions, it is the physician more than anyone perhaps

[1] Chase, Stuart, *The Proper Study of Mankind*, 1948; Childe, V. G., *Social Evolution*, 1952; Kroeber, A. L., "So-called Social Science," 1936; Leighton, A. H., *Human Relations in a Changing World*, 1949; Linton, Ralph, editor, *The Science of Man in the World Crisis*, 1945; MacIver, R. M., *Social Causation*, 1942; Malinowski, Bronislaw, *A Scientific Theory of Culture*, 1944; Ogburn, W. F., *Social Change*, rev. 1950; Sumner, W. G., and A. G. Keller, *The Science of Society*, 1927, vol. 1.

who must rely on the biophysical sciences and also deal daily with an abundance of psychosocial data relevant to the individual's adaptations. He may study firsthand in the same body, and often focused in the same organs, the combined effects of biophysical and psychosocial forces in operation. In short, he is in a position to look both ways and to achieve a more integrated and comprehensive perspective.

Why has not the physician done more of this? For one thing, only recently has he recognized that forgotten or unconscious motivations in the lives of his patients, associated with especially stressful social situations, can provoke reaction patterns that may damage certain of their organs—heart, stomach, respiratory system, and so on. Medical men in general are just beginning to search systematically for behavioral processes and guiding concepts that go beneath the level of organic lesions and identifiable physical disorders. The recognition of unconscious, disguised, and automatic personal and social dynamics, as well as the more easily observed stresses in the individual's adaptations, has introduced into the behavioral sciences and medicine something that is profound and maybe prophetic.

We must remember, however, that we are still under the impact of an epoch of amazing progress in the physical sciences which nearly eclipsed for a time medical interests in their social counterparts. Accordingly, the clinical portrayals of the patient often tend to overlook his personal and social involvements as a result of preoccupation with his case history as an organism. Neither the extraordinary successes nor the therapeutic ineptitudes and failures on the personal and social side of the medical care are usually accorded the sober scrutiny and systematic study that has become routine for similar successes or failures on the strictly physical side. This may be explained in part by the late development of the behavioral sciences, but it may also be attributed to the tendency of medical men to block with a pervasive skepticism any interest on their part in the personal and social components of disease. They often raise rhetorically such questions as "What, after all, have the behavioral sciences to offer medicine?" Since medical problems are acknowledged to involve important personal and social factors, would it not be more constructive to reformulate the question thus: "How can we as medical men work with the social scientists in the accumulation of new knowledge and skills for the preservation of health and the treatment of sick people?"

We have already indicated that a change in outlook is becoming apparent, with greater concern being shown for the emotional and social components in disease and its treatment. The fact that in spite of the amazing triumphs over contagious diseases our hospitals are still crowded with incapacitated people leads to increasing medical interest in the so-called functional disorders and other less-well-understood ailments. Added to this are recent developments in the behavioral sciences, such as the study of stress in social relationships, which serve to support the present shift in interest. This expansion of medical horizon with respect to what may be involved in an illness is indicated by the greater concern in "the patient as a person," the search for social variables in disease, the formulation of new goals in comprehensive patient care (or even family care), and the growth of programs of teamwork in therapy and rehabilitation. In addition, there are new formulations of the role of the "personal physician" and varied experimental projects in prepayment and group insurance for extended medical security.

In summary, there is now emerging within the medical profession a more systematic concern for the personal and social factors in illness and a more forthright recognition of medical responsibility for comprehensive safeguards against them. Indeed, some physicians point out the inherent paradox in medical programs that treat patients by procedures based solely upon physical etiology or causation and neglect consideration of the psychosocial components. They recognize that such treatment can prove self-defeating and may actually worsen the patient's condition, in spite of very competent medical care on a strictly physical basis. Thus, a growing segment of the medical profession is devoting considerable interest to the study of the psychosocial elements in ill health and to ways of putting such knowledge to the most effective use.

However, before these goals can be effectively attained, the alliance between medicine and social science must be carefully nurtured. Regular channels of communication must be established and utilized, facts and insights from the physical and social sciences shared and integrated, and new conceptual formulations provided for the promotion of research toward better medical service and better science.

The present volume makes a step in that direction. It is an effort to set some of the fundamental social science concepts within a medical context and to endow them with significant meaning for medical personnel, so that they will be able to appreciate more fully the patient's personal problems as a member of society and make use of this understanding in the treatment of illness.

CHAPTER 2

Backgrounds and Perspectives in Medicine and Social Science

THE GROWING AWARENESS that medicine and social science share many areas of common concern is in line with historical developments in the physical sciences. In chemistry, physics, and biology, as new problems arose that resisted solution in terms of traditional concepts, it was found necessary to cross interdisciplinary boundaries and seek scientific allies. We have witnessed, for example, the emergence of biochemistry, biophysics, and physical chemistry as new fields of specialization representing cross-linkages of scientific personnel, concepts, and methods. In this process the identity of the parent sciences was not at all blurred. Each represented accumulations of basic knowledge useful for collaboration and gained new orientations and skills for identifying and investigating problems of joint concern.

This same process is becoming apparent with respect to medicine and social science. There are problems in medicine that transcend traditional, organized medical knowledge and that are leading some medical experts toward the exploration of sociological variables in health and disease. This requires alliance and collaboration with those disciplines that have studied human adaptations from the standpoint of group processes and cultural dynamics. It is not essential that either medicine or the social sciences abandon their primary concern or concepts, but each discipline must achieve new orientations and perspectives in promoting joint undertakings.

Just as earlier there came an opportune time for linking medicine with such specialized sciences as anatomy, physiology, neurology, and so on, with outstanding gains, so now the new union with the social sciences offers promise of further advancement in the understanding and control of illness. Perhaps these present developments can be better appreciated if we review the separate lines of expansion that have brought the two disciplines to a common meeting place—focus on the individual in his social environment.

DEVELOPMENTS IN MEDICAL SCIENCE

The development of medicine as a science has taken place almost entirely within the modern era of the western world, and its advances have been the product chiefly of the prime centers of western civilization, Europe and America. During the vast stretches of man's previous history, and even at present over great parts of the world, the medical arts have remained tied to superstitious customs involving little or no knowledge of the human body. Attitudes toward sickness were interwoven with religious conceptions, and treatment was in the hands of the *shaman*, or medicine man, who was often more priest than physician.[1] At the same time, many folk remedies held elements of empirical value because they represented the accumulated trial-and-error experience of previous generations, and had survived in the culture as a consequence of their effective-

[1] Ackerknecht, E. H., "Natural Diseases and Rational Treatment in Primitive Medicine," 1946; *Idem*, "On the Collecting of Data Concerning Primitive Medicine," 1945; *Idem*, "Primitive Medicine and Culture Pattern," 1942; *Idem*, "Primitive Surgery," 1947; *Idem*, "Problems of Primitive Medicine," 1942; *Idem*, "Psychopathology, Primitive Medicine, and Primitive Culture," 1943; Charles, L. H., *Drama in Shaman Exorcism*, 1953; Corlett, W. T., *The Medicine-Man of the American Indian*, 1935; Devereux, George, "Primitive Psychiatry," 1940–1942; Elkin, A. P., *Aboriginal Men of High Degree*, 1946; Evans-Pritchard, E. E., *Witchcraft, Oracles, and Magic Among the Azande*, 1937; Ferguson, E. A., *The Theory and Practice of Medicine Among Preliterate Peoples*, 1947; Field, M. J., *Religion and Medicine of the Gã People*, 1937; Greenlee, R. F., "Medicine and Curing Practices of the Modern Florida Seminoles," 1944; Hallowell, A. I., *The Role of Conjuring in Saulteaux Society*, 1942; Kluckhohn, Clyde, *Navaho Witchcraft*, 1944; Maddox, J. L., *The Medicine Man*, 1923; Morgan, William, "Navaho Treatment of Sickness," 1931; Paul, B. D., "Mental Disorders and Self-Regulating Processes in Culture," 1953; Rivers, W. H. R., *Medicine, Magic, and Religion*, 1924; Sigerist, H. E., *A History of Medicine*, 1951, vol. 1; Stone, Eric, *Medicine Among the American Indians*, 1932.

ness. Without even an elementary knowledge of the structure of the body or the nature of disease, moreover, the medicine man and his helpers were often able to effect remarkable cures because they paid considerable attention to the bearing of emotions, attitudes, and social pressures or supports upon sickness and health, and made active even though unsophisticated use of these psychosocial elements in therapy. Some of this understanding and skill has been retained all along the way and also refined in the present-day relationships of the physician to his patients; but it has only recently become the object of scientific interest in general medical care and in the relationship of the entire therapeutic team.

It is easy to understand how medicine, confronted with the amazing achievements of the rapidly striding natural sciences, was compelled to break with its mystical past and adopt a new credo. As a result, from the beginning of the scientific era, the developing methods and viewpoint of the "pure" sciences were turned upon the human body to the neglect of its "spirit." The structure of the body, its functions, and the diseases that plague it, have since then been studied chiefly within the physicochemical or biophysical frames of reference. Consequently, the distinctive nature of man as a person and the essential oneness of his psychic and organic life have been largely overlooked.

The great "laboratory period" of medicine has been brilliant and productive. One by one, many of the mysteries of man's organic nature have been unraveled. During the Renaissance, methods of autopsy were developed which made possible for the first time a precise study of the details of the human organism. The skeletal structure and skeletal muscles were first painstakingly mapped out. Later, in the seventeenth century, the forward bounds of physics under the leadership of Galileo and Newton brought application of physical principles to the human body, and Harvey produced his study of the heart and the circulation of the blood. A hundred years afterward the problems of circulation were skillfully investigated from a quantitative point of view by another Englishman, Stephen Hales. Late in the eighteenth century when chemistry was making signal advances, physiology profited from the new knowledge, particularly in the investigation of respiration, in the comparison between living organisms and other agencies of oxidation, and in a new appreciation of the nature of the digestive processes.

Stemming from these and other pioneering efforts, the nineteenth and early twentieth centuries represented the great productive period of this laboratory approach. As the result of experiment, observation, and dissection, the various organs of the human body and the systems by which they function, each in turn, yielded to analysis. The fundamental postulate of this era of investigation was that living organisms could be understood in terms of biophysics and chemistry, and it was in such terms that medicine set about the study of disease and its treatment.

This orientation led logically to detailed analysis of the physical mechanisms in the human body. The principal aim in the exploration of the causes of disease was the localization of pathological processes, with the search limited largely to identifying local morphological changes in tissue. This laboratory approach led to fundamental achievements in understanding and combating disease, as set forth in modern bacteriology, pharmacology, and surgery. With the discovery and identification of germs and other micro-organisms, an epoch was launched in which great categories of infectious diseases have been brought largely under control.

The very brilliance and progress of this age and the amazing fruits of this particularistic method of research led, however, to a somewhat one-sided development. It blurred the fundamental fact that the organism functions as one unit, which is goal-striving, and that each part can be thoroughly understood only in relation to the whole and in terms of its strivings.

Disease usually meant *not* what happened to the whole man but what happened to his organs. The approach to diseases largely turned into the task of localizing the defect to one or another part, classifying it in terms of known groups of diseases, and treating it in a prescribed manner. Medical scientists became so engrossed with the accumulating mass of data concerning specific diseases and their manifestations that they lost interest for a time in the search for new perspectives.

Renewed Medical Interest in the Whole Person

While the science of medicine at first took little notice of the fact, there has always been, as we have seen, wide popular recognition that a man who feels threatened exhibits changes in his physical organism relevant to his health. The heart that beats faster with rage or fear, the palm that sweats with anxiety, the shudder of terror, the chill of grief, all bore gross testimony to such connections. But partly because these effects were presumably of a passing nature, and therefore not relevant to organ damage, no great attention was given to them by medical science.

At about this time, growing knowledge in experimental neurology helped to pave the way for a more comprehensive understanding of the interrelationships of different parts of the body. All parts were shown to be connected more or less closely with the central governing mechanisms of the nervous system. While the involuntary or autonomic nervous system helped mainly to regulate internal bodily processes, the voluntary or somatic nervous system subserved the external organs that dealt with the outer environment. The autonomic nervous system, involved in dilation of the pupils, secretion of saliva, slowing of the heart, production of perspiration, erection of the hair, and contraction of the blood vessels, indicated the occurrence of a relationship between internal bodily processes and feelings, attitudes, and emotions. Moreover the skeletal muscles and joints supported by both systems become extensively involved in such emotional and behavioral adjustments to threats, as is conspicuously shown by tremors, tics, twitchings, and spasms. The full implications of such relationships were, however, for the time not extensively explored.

Investigations of the functions of the ductless glands, a comparatively recent development of medical science, gave evidence from biochemical analysis of the relationship between emotional and personality factors and the internal mechanisms of the body. The glands are involved in chemical regulation of the body through secretion of specific substances into the blood stream, and prove to be responsive to the needs and purposes of the individual through delicate connections with the cerebrum and the autonomic nervous system. Thus, for instance, the adrenal gland, by the discharge of adrenalin in times of danger, helps to mobilize the body for action. Moreover, these glands prove to have continuing functions, and to vary in their activity from individual to individual. Researches in this field thus served to spur the movement for a more synthetic and unified approach to the study of man and his diseases.[1]

Interconnections of a different kind were brought to light through observation and study of individuals with so-called "hysterical" manifestations. Certain patients exhibited symptoms, chiefly disturbances of the sensory and motor functions, for which no gross structural basis could be found. The fact that these symptoms could be made to disappear during hypnosis suggested the hypothesis that they were attempts to discharge by acting out the tensions resulting from serious emotional conflicts. In his early researches with hypnosis, Freud found that such patients under hypnosis brought forth startling revelations of their emotional conflicts. He came to

[1] Alexander, Franz, *Psychosomatic Medicine*, 1950; Cannon, W. B., *Bodily Changes in Pain, Hunger, Fear and Rage*, 1929; Idem, *The Wisdom of the Body*, 1939; Cobb, Stanley, *Emotions and Clinical Medicine*, 1950; Galdston, Iago, *editor*, *Beyond the Germ Theory*, 1954; Gellhorn, Ernst, *Autonomic Regulations*, 1943; Reymert, M. L., editor, *Feelings and Emotions*, 1950.

classify such manifestations under the heading "conversion hysteria." From these discoveries stemmed studies of the role of the unconscious in human behavior, and the protective reactive mechanisms that operate in human adaptation.[1]

Paralleling these findings were the discoveries by interested physicians concerning "functional" ailments. Disturbances were found in the performance of certain of the internal organs such as the stomach, the bowel, the cardiovascular system, for which no gross structural basis could be found; even the most careful study with the microscope of removed or dead tissues could reveal no discernible morphological changes. Only the coordination and intensity of function of the organ was disturbed, often without initial change in its anatomic structure. Physicians came to postulate that the occurrence of such ailments might be related to the maladjustments of the individual, the organ's performance being influenced through its connections with the central and autonomic nervous systems. In this light, treatment was often directed toward helping the patient change his goals, attitudes, or way of life, or helping him realize the importance of working himself out of his difficulties. If circumstances were favorable, if the pattern of abreaction was not too deeply ingrained, the bodily derangements were often reversible. Thus, they were regarded as less serious than "organic" disorders.

However, the relevance of such inappropriate adaptive reactions to "physical" disease was further emphasized when clinicians began to suspect that long-endured "functional" disorders may gradually lead to serious "organic" difficulties or those with irreversible morphological changes. Indeed, there is rapidly accumulating evidence that such may be the case. These ailments are seen to advance through two stages. First, the normal operation of a part or a bodily system is altered in performance—amount, duration, or pace—as a part of the individual reaction to a threatening situation; and

[1] Jones, Ernest, *The Life and Work of Sigmund Freud*, 1953, vol. 1.

second, the chronic or vigorous functional disturbance leads to tissue damage and sometimes to irreversible disease of organs and systems.[1]

The Relation of Stress and Disease

A working hypothesis formulated by Wolff and his associates suggests that protective reactions are primarily elicited in response to dangerous physical, chemical, or electrical noxious stimuli, and that these same patterns so used in an appropriate and useful manner may be subsequently evoked by symbols of danger or threat. They are then less appropriate, and therefore may do harm.

Also, according to this view, protective reactions are *not* "chain" reactions, in which the individual first "feels" (fear, anxiety, hostility, and so on), which is then followed by altered bodily function (gut, heart, skeletal muscles, and so on), and ultimately by abnormal behavior. Indeed, changed behavior, feelings, attitudes, and bodily states are all seen as parts of the reaction to the threat and hence not causally related to each other. It is emphasized that feelings, bodily adjustments, and behavior alter concurrently in reaction to threats, and in varying relative amounts. Although protective reactions in a given individual are usually predictable as to dominance and order of occurrence during stress, one reaction may prevail to such a degree as to hide the others. Such dominance may shift during the life of an individual from one constellation to another. For example, a man in reaction to a situation in his family that caused him to feel humiliated and to develop ulcerative colitis, was ostensibly tranquil, inactive, and cooperative in behavior.

[1] For summaries of developments in psychosomatic medicine, the reader is referred to: Dunbar, H. F., *Psychosomatic Diagnosis*, 1943; Idem, *Mind and Body* 1947; Idem, *Synopsis of Psychosomatic Diagnosis and Treatment*, 1948; Garrett, J. F., editor, *Psychological Aspects of Physical Disability*, 1952; Halliday, J. L., *Psychosocial Medicine*, 1948; Seidenfeld, M. A., *Psychological Aspects of Medical Care*, 1949; Selye, Hans, "The General Adaptation Syndrome and the Diseases of Adaptation," 1946; Weiss, Edward, and O. S. English, *Psychosomatic Medicine*, 1949; *Proceedings* of the Association for Research in Nervous and Mental Disease, 1950: *Life Stress and Bodily Disease*.

Then, some time later, still in the same setting, with exacerbation of bad relations with his family, the colitis abruptly ended, and he became extremely restless, deeply depressed, uncooperative, and attempted suicide. In brief, different protective or adaptive reactions are not causally related (that is, anxiety *does not* cause dyspepsia) but are separate, though interrelated, adjustment patterns.

The thesis to be considered in this essay may be epitomized as follows. The stress accruing from a situation is based in large part on the way the affected subject perceives it: perception depends upon a multiplicity of factors including the genetic equipment, basic individual needs and longings, earlier conditioning influences, and a host of life experiences and cultural pressures. No one of these can be singled out for exclusive emphasis but since man is a tribal creature, sociocultural forces are important. The common denominator of stress disorders is reaction to circumstances of threatening significance to the organism. Such stress reactions are shown to be relevant to disease.

The particular adaptation pattern evoked by a noxious agent or threat is the resultant of past life experience that conditions individuals to react in specific ways. Hence "etiology" in disease becomes a function not merely of precipitating incident and setting but largely of the past of the individual and the group with which he is identified.

Protective reaction patterns are evoked in given individuals by threats of highly particularized significance. It has been shown that these threats or situations evoke entirely different bodily responses in different persons, although when a threat evokes a particular adaptive pattern, the reaction often can be seen to include specifically related attitudes, feelings, and behavior.

Medical Interest in Life Histories

Such a widening of medical horizons on the nature and origins of illness is leading to a new interest in, and concern for, the life history of the individual. As a human being, an integrated unit with fears, aspirations, goals, despairs, and compulsions which profoundly affect his physical make-up, the patient as a person and a product of his past experience is becoming the legitimate object of medical study. The line formerly conceived to divide sharply his organic processes from his emotional and social life is now seen to be an artificial one, and many kinds of research and analysis have as their aim a more synthesized over-all approach to his problems.

The reactions to stresses and strains in the person's mental and emotional life and the "attitudinal sets" which he acquires in his relationships with intimate associates are seen to accumulate and to express themselves in personal crises, often overdramatized. Such repeated emergency adaptations become habitual and result in sets of protective and defensive reaction patterns to certain life situations that are overly challenging, threatening, or otherwise intolerable for the individual. Typical run-of-the-mill examples of such pressures in our society may be the need to get ahead, to live up to reputation and role, to make money, to provide for a family, to make a name for oneself, to achieve "success," and so on. Such pressures may become for a particular person overbearing, pushing him into impractical strivings, overwrought anxieties, inappropriate responses, and consequent abuse of his biological capacities. It is becoming evident that a person's life situations and his ill-suited reactions to perceived threats therein correlate significantly with certain of his physical ailments; in short, that his "way of life" has conditioned his acquirement of the disease and his adaptations to it.[1]

While it is assumed that certain diseases are more closely associated with social pressures and personality characteristics

[1] These factors are ably discussed in the following books: Faris, R. E. L., *Social Disorganization*, 1948; Kershaw, J. D., *An Approach to Social Medicine*, 1946; Mannheim, Karl, *Man and Society in an Age of Reconstruction*, 1940; Robinson, G. C., *The Patient as a Person*, 1939; Selye, Hans, *The Physiology and Pathology of Exposure to Stress*, 1950; Wolff, H. G., *Stress and Disease*, 1953.

than others, apparently no clinician is wise enough to say which are entirely free of such influences, including the infectious diseases. In clinical case histories the affinity of the person for his ailment is often easily surmised by the physician or, indeed, suspected by a discerning patient himself. But how to unravel and deal effectively with the complex set of factors involved presents a challenge to medicine that relates its interest to those of the social sciences and brings into sharp focus the patient as a goal-directed person in society.

DEVELOPMENTS IN THE SOCIAL SCIENCES

Although the findings of medical science have always been recognized as having a direct bearing upon man's welfare, the theoretical formulations of the social sciences remained for a long time within the province of the obscure and the scholarly and have only in recent decades reached a stage of development where their practical usefulness has begun to win wider acknowledgment. As applied to medical care, this new recognition has been chiefly the result of the light social science has shed upon the problems of the individual human being as a group member within a particular society and culture, and the possible influence of such factors upon his health and well-being.

Study of man as a social being may be traced back to the philosophical speculations of the early Greeks and their successors in later eras; but previous to the past century, such study was largely the fruit of rational thought, was distorted by the prejudices of the time and place, and was based only to a limited extent upon the empirical data that would make it qualify as genuine scientific research. A more objective perspective was largely the result of the opening up of vast new areas of the world where human beings were found to be living with beliefs and customs so far different from those of the dominant civilizations that established convictions regarding the nature of man had to be thrown into the discard.

It became apparent that man's ways of acting, feeling, and believing could be explained only by postulating the existence of a further element, interposed between man and his environment, which helps to shape all his adaptations to his physical milieu and to his fellows. This elusive and all-important element in human life, of which thinkers in earlier times were only dimly aware, has come in modern social science to be known as culture.[1]

Recognition of this important x-factor has served as one of the cornerstones for the building of a science of human behavior in which the various social sciences, especially anthropology, sociology, and social psychology, that had previously pursued relatively independent courses, are now uniting. In the brief historical sketch below, cultural studies are considered chiefly within the framework of anthropology, which has done the principal spadework in the field and collected much of the basic primary data on group life in other than western cultures. But this device is largely one of convenience. At every step other social sciences have made major contributions to our knowledge of culture, society, and the human individual, and they have been integrated into the general framework within which all branches of science now press forward.[2]

[1] For representative examples, consult: Herskovits, M. J., *Man and His Works*, 1948; Kluckhohn, Clyde, *Mirror for Man*, 1949; Kroeber, A. L., editor, *Anthropology Today*, 1953; *Idem*, "The Concept of Culture in Science," 1949; Linton, Ralph, *The Study of Man*, 1936; Lowie, R. H., *A History of Ethnological Theory*, 1937; Malinowski, Bronislaw, *A Scientific Theory of Culture*, 1944; *Idem*, "Culture as a Determinant of Behavior," 1936; *Idem*, "Man's Culture and Man's Behavior," 1941–1942; Mühlmann, W. E., *Geschichte der Anthropologie*, 1948; Murdock, G. P., "The Science of Culture," 1932; *Idem*, "Bronislaw Malinowski," 1943; Róheim, Géza, *The Origin and Function of Culture*, 1943; Sapir, Edward, "Culture, Genuine and Spurious," 1924; *Idem*, "Cultural Anthropology and Psychiatry," 1932; White, L. A., *The Science of Culture*, 1949; *Idem*, "History, Evolution, and Functionalism," 1945.

[2] Provocative attempts at integrating the social sciences have been made by: Evans-Pritchard, E. E., *Social Anthropology*, 1951; Gillin, John, *The Ways of Men*, 1948; Lewin, Kurt, *Field Theory in Social Science*, 1951; MacIver, R. M., *Social Causation*, 1942; Merton, R. K., *Social Theory and Social Structure*, 1949; Parsons, Talcott, *The Social System*, 1951; Parsons, Talcott, and E. A. Shils, editors, *Toward a General Theory of Action*, 1951.

Early Developments in Anthropology

For many years anthropologists relied upon museum collections and the racy reports of explorers, travelers, traders, and political emissaries for the facts out of which to formulate their theories of culture. It is common knowledge that these early students of man, the so-called "museum moles" and "armchair scholars" took a forward stride when they decided to spend part of their time in the ethnographic field. They began to observe directly the behavior of their more primitive contemporaries and to share their experience. They undertook to gather firsthand, and "on the hoof" so to speak, the relevant and vital data with which to check and revise their theories.

This step beyond books and museums could hardly approximate the methods of the scientific laboratory. It has usually been impossible, except within very confined limits, to test social formulations in a controlled situation and under planned experimental procedure.[1] Even for the investigator in the field, human beings in group life do not easily lend themselves to such manipulation, especially when the observer is a stranger and of alien background.

Anthropologists therefore adopted methods of observing and systematically recording the behavior of man in those laboratory setups within which nature performs its own experiments on human beings—the countless societies the world over, each with a separate and somewhat different culture. Primitive peoples were particularly well adapted to such study and analysis. In these small, relatively isolated tribes, free from the complexities and manifold relationships of more advanced civilizations, a field worker could observe some of the

[1] Chapin, F. S., *Experimental Designs in Sociological Research*, 1947; Dodd, S. C., *A Controlled Experiment on Rural Hygiene in Syria*, 1934; Greenwood, Ernest, *Experimental Sociology*, 1944; Herskovits, M. J., "The Ethnographic Laboratory," 1948; Lewis, Oscar, "Controls and Experiments in Field Work," 1953; Lippitt, R., "The Strategy of Sociopsychological Research," 1950; Rose, A. M., "Conditions of the Social Science Experiment," 1948; Sherif, Muzafer, "Some Methodological Remarks Related to Experimentation in Social Psychology," 1947.

infinite variety of ways in which culture can shape the behavior and attitudes of man.

For scientific purposes the adoption of a systematic scheme for recording cultural phenomena in specific time and place settings marked an important step forward. By this means the form and content of a culture, and its relation to the physical environment, could be set down and compared with that of other cultures in order to study the circumstances and the organized forces within which the lives of a particular group of people could and did find expression.

For the time, in anthropology, this proved a most fruitful approach. The field worker endured considerable personal discomfort and labored diligently to acquire and document data concerning the different cultures: the varied conditions under which people are found to survive; the cultural patterns that compel, limit, or otherwise influence their attitudes and behavior; and the dynamics of cultural change. In such a manner, anthropology became in a major sense *situational* in character, *descriptive* in content, *broad* in scope, and *comparative* in method.

A gross classification of the data assembled fell under the rubrics *organic and superorganic phenomena*. Classed under *organic* elements of societal life were such items as the physiological characteristics of the people; the physical environment with its climate, flora, fauna, and so forth; the material equipment shaped by the hands of man; the source, type, and means of subsistence. These organic elements provided, of course, the physical base and framework which limited as well as influenced the less material elements of the culture.[1] Included under *superorganic*[2] were the social systems of group organization and relationships (the economic institutions, the family, religion, and government); the manifest and inferred goals and norms of human strivings; the meaningful interpretations of past and present experiences; the rules and codes of conduct;

[1] See Murdock, G. P., and others, *Outline of Cultural Materials*, 1945.

[2] Kroeber, A. L., "The Superorganic," 1917; Spencer, Herbert, *Principles of Sociology*, 1896; Sumner, W. G., and A. G. Keller, *The Science of Society*, 1927, vol. 1.

and the socially sanctioned rewards and penalties for compliance and breaches in prescribed behavior.

This *context approach* for comparative purposes, and for the formulation of broad generalizations about man, his capacity, and his culture prevailed throughout a long and very productive period. Vast accumulations of data were assembled and classified from a random, but worldwide, sample of surviving tribes. These many invaluable ethnographic reports constitute our primary documentary sources in anthropological literature. In broad perspective the aim was eventually to bring together for comparative studies an adequate sample of cultures that would portray the most comprehensive range of patterned contexts for human behavior in all its existing, if not in all its possible, manifestations. Thus, in brief, cultural anthropology first came into its own as a context-centered, rather than a person-focused, science.

All this was essentially a study of tribal systems, an examination and comparison of cultural settings into which numbers of human beings are born, live through the cycle of their lives, and pass out of life in a more or less prescribed and predictable manner. The formulation implied that the biological organisms, that is, the individuals, may come and go but that the sociocultural system has an existence of its own and goes on to fulfill its independent destiny, limited only by the capacities of the organisms and the circumstances of the physical environment. Efforts were made to discover and to formulate the principles and processes common to all such societal systems.[1]

In laboratory parlance, emphasis was placed on the varied and variable forms and forces within the *maze* (of culture) rather than on the individuality of the persons who, like rodents, run their course within the prescribed setup. Nor was much attention paid to the consequence of maze-running

[1] Excellent summaries of this general approach are to be found in Briffault, Robert, *The Mothers*, 1927; Lippert, Julius, *Kulturgeschichte der Menschheit ihrem organischen Aufbau*, 1886; Lowie, R. H., *A History of Ethnological Theory*, 1937; Sumner, W. G., and A. G. Keller, *The Science of Society*, 1927.

for any members of the group. Indeed, in the growth and development of the *culture*, any particular individuals were regarded as replaceable, if not interchangeable, units who fitted into the social pattern, or were eliminated because they did not fit. *The maze was the thing*. There arose in anthropology, therefore, a rationale that justified ignoring individuals except as informants and specimens who revealed through their behavior the patterns and pressures of their culture.

Moreover, from the comparative studies of many different cultures, anthropologists came to view man as a tribal being rather than as a biological creature. At first, they were impressed much more by the diversities in cultural patterns and the consequent deviations in individual adaptations among the tribes than by the basic uniformities and limitations in human behavior. Whenever queries arose concerning a particular way of coping with a specified need or problem, a stock ethnographic answer came to be: "Well, some do and some don't." There usually followed statements of fantastically variable practices, inspiring the idea that other instances could be discovered even farther off center. Thus, at least in folklore, almost any imaginable conduct appeared to be standard practice somewhere. This attention to cultural differences that shaped human behavior within so wide a range of variations continued for a long time. Valiant attempts were made to visit the most isolated tribes and to document the most outlandish customs before they should become corrupted by civilization or disappear from the face of the earth, with some significant oddity of behavior lost, perhaps forever, to social science.

As a consequence of these developments in anthropology, two kindred and somewhat radical concepts arose with respect to culture and human nature: the principle of cultural *relativity*[1] and the theory of individual *pliability*. Students of culture set forth the thesis that there are few cultural norms, or preferred standards of behavior, that apply universally. They also

[1] See Herskovits, M. J., "The Problem of Cultural Relativism," 1948.

held that biological factors may seldom, if ever, determine the specific patterns of individual adaptation, except in gross and obvious ways, such as providing *in some manner* for the necessity of eating, breathing, elimination, rest, and so on. Indeed, by the stronger proponents of the theory, the biological propensities were hardly regarded as limiting elements when behavior was viewed from the perspective of the great variety of adaptations that existed. Granting the possibility in the physical environment, it was assumed that a culture could move in almost any direction, imposing its patterns upon the participants, and making any biologically feasible behavior standard and proper. Also, individuals could be conditioned and acculturated into any one of an unknown variety of adaptations, proving the human organism to be amazingly modifiable.

These concepts wrought havoc with our traditional and long-cherished ideals concerning philosophical verities and ethical values and, above all, with the theory that human behavior is biologically patterned and instinct-determined. Even our inalienable natural rights and the so-called noble instincts became subject to challenge. For a time the new concepts in one form or another held sway in the behavioral sciences.

It is worth while to reiterate that during this period in anthropology the center of interest was on the culturally patterned forms, processes, and relationships, with a strong tendency to discount or ignore individuals as vital, directive, and limiting agents in society. The culture was endowed with a life of its own and the individuals were made to appear as short-span, pliable specimens of the system who could be expected to comply like puppets to the strings that culture pulled. To be sure, one would fail to respond and fall out here and there, but others would take their place, and the show would go on.

For our purpose, what these earlier field studies in culture add up to can be briefly summarized as follows. They provide clearer formulations and more efficient techniques for the analysis and interpretation of the societal systems that everywhere in the world constitute the framework of man's group life. They point up the independent variables within these systems and give some understanding of the relationship of these forces to one another, and some knowledge of the processes and the course of change that the systems undergo. They build up a factual and detailed foundation in cultural contrasts that serves to qualify overdrawn conclusions concerning the fixed norms, the established procedures, and the innately determined drives and limitations reflected in a particular society. They embody a wide sampling of the cultures that man in group life has gradually built up and superimposed upon his biological nature and his physical environment.

These older students of man and his culture were thorough in charting the group-derived systems of human relations and in checking the patterns of man's socially acquired behavior in general. Their theories, however, were little concerned with, and also inadequate for, clarifying the reciprocal relationships of the individual to his society and his culture, nor did they trace the effects of these relationships upon the human being as a person and as a physical organism. They surveyed and outlined the variable sociocultural situations within which man makes his adjustments, but they did not attempt, systematically, to assay the impact of the situation upon the particular man. As will be shown later, these former contributions of anthropology are invaluable as frames of reference for the more recent theories and studies concerned with the dynamics of individual adaptations to life stress and bodily disease within social context.

Cultural Configurations in Limited Situations

During the past two or three decades many anthropologists have moved from the broad, comparative approach in the study of culture toward a detailed and systematic analysis of concrete situations in tribal or areal context with the intention of portraying more precisely the dynamics involved in cultural integration and in interpersonal and group relationships. This more specific approach, exemplified by such students as Malinowski, Firth, Mead, Sapir, Benedict, and others, has stimulated new interest in the functional aspects of culture and the manner in which the personnel, the participating members of a particular society, are made to fit into the system.[1]

Here the influence of advances in other fields of inquiry is apparent. Sociological interest in unifying principles, adaptive processes, and integrating mechanisms had begun to narrow in range from analysis of the total social order to study of the community in cultural context and in contemporary as well as primitive societies. Moreover, new knowledge from the schools of psychology and psychiatry in their various forms was becoming a valuable aid in the task of charting out the chief channels through which culture shapes the individual as a personality and, perchance, leaves its mark upon him as an organism.[2] A new approach thus appeared fruitful to anthropologists: detailed studies of specific and limited sociocultural situations where the dynamics of culture and their bearing upon the individual could be analyzed.

[1] See, for example, Bennett, J. W., and M. M. Tumin, *Social Life*, 1949; Goldschmidt, W. R., "Ethics and the Structure of Society," 1951; Hertzler, J. O., *Social Institutions*, 1946; Lévi-Strauss, Claude, "Social Structure," 1953; Lowie, R. H., *Social Organization*, 1948; Malinowski, Bronislaw, *Argonauts of the Western Pacific*, 1922; Idem, *Crime and Custom in Savage Society*, 1926; Idem, *Coral Gardens and Their Magic*, 1935; *Idem*, "The Group and the Individual in Functional Analysis," 1939; Murdock, G. P., *Social Structure*, 1949; Radcliffe-Brown, A. R., *Structure and Function in Primitive Society*, 1952; Redfield, Robert, *The Folk Culture of Yucatan*, 1941; *Idem*, "The Folk Society," 1947.

[2] Recent general works in social psychology from psychological, anthropological, or sociological backgrounds are representative of these developments. Consult, for example, from psychology: Bonner, Hubert, *Social Psychology*, 1953; Cantril, Hadley, *The Psychology of Social Movements*, 1941; Coutu, Walter, *Emergent Human Nature*, 1949; Klineberg, Otto, *Social Psychology*, 1940; Koffka, Kurt, *Principles of Gestalt Psychology*, 1935; Lindesmith, A. R., and A. L. Strauss, *Social Psychology*, 1949; Shaffer, L. F., *The Psychology of Adjustment*, 1936; Sherif, Muzafer, *An Outline of Social Psychology*, 1948; Sherif, M., and H. Cantril, *The Psychology of Ego-Involvements*, 1947.

From anthropology: Evans-Pritchard, E. E., *Social Anthropology*, 1951; Slotkin, J. S., *Social Anthropology*, 1950; Warner, W. L., and Leo Srole, *The Social Systems of American Ethnic Groups*, 1945.

From sociology: Cooley, C. H., *Human Nature and the Social Order*, 1902; Faris, R. E. L., *Social Psychology*, 1952; La Piere, R. T., and P. R. Farnsworth, *Social Psychology*, 1949; Mead, G. H., *Mind, Self and Society*, 1934; Newcomb, T. M., *Social Psychology*, 1950; Schermerhorn, R. A., "Social Psychiatry," 1953.

In the wake of these developments, the concept of cultural relativity has given way to one of cultural *relevance*, and the principle of human plasticity is subject to qualifications in the light of newly acquired data regarding the biological nature of man. The sky is no longer the conceptual limit to what a given culture may contain nor are the adaptations which an individual can make under pressure from his culture regarded as limitless.

The concept of relevance as applied to culture in specific context has brought to the fore strong recognition of consistent fitting together, or *configuration*, of the various parts of a particular culture.[1] It gives point to the principle, which Sumner in sociology had earlier emphasized, that culture exerts an internal "strain towards consistency" on all its component elements and produces an integrated whole. Thus, in concrete social situations, there may be found a pertinent and interwoven relevance of each part to the total pattern, as Malinowski perhaps first conclusively demonstrated in his studies of the Trobriand Islanders.[2] This viewpoint has also made clear the fact that processes of cultural change and growth are subject to regularities much more specific than "historical accidents" or gross additions. Anything simply does not "go" for that culture which is now viewed as *selective*, in an automatic way, toward innovations and variations. Systematic studies now attempt to demonstrate how the varied parts of a specific cul-

[1] Important sources include: Benedict, Ruth, *Patterns of Culture*, 1934; *Idem*, "Continuities and Discontinuities in Cultural Conditioning," 1938; Gillin, John, "The Configuration Problem in Culture," 1936; Gorer, Geoffrey, "Themes in Japanese Culture," 1943; Kluckhohn, Clyde, "Patterning as Exemplified in Navajo Culture," 1941; Malinowski, Bronislaw, "The Group and the Individual in Functional Analysis," 1939; Mandelbaum, D. G., "Social Trends and Personal Pressures," 1941; Opler, M. E., "Themes as Dynamic Forces in Culture," 1945; *Idem*, "An Application of the Theory of Themes in Culture," 1946; Sapir, Edward, "The Unconscious Patterning of Behavior in Society," 1928; Simmons, L. W., "Statistical Correlations in the Science of Society," 1937; White, L. A., "Kroeber's Configurations of Culture Growth," 1946.

[2] Malinowski, Bronislaw, *Argonauts of the Western Pacific*, 1922; Idem, *Coral Gardens and Their Magic*, 1935; Idem, *Crime and Custom in Savage Society*, 1926; Idem, *Sex and Repression in Savage Society*, 1927; Idem, *The Sexual Life of Savages in Northwestern Melanesia*, 1929.

tural system all "hang together," and how the culture adopts and assimilates new and suitable elements while rejecting ill-fitting ones. They also direct attention to the individual's place in the total scheme, how he is molded to its dictates, and the manner and extent to which this exerts hardship upon him.[1]

Linked with this newer approach to the study of culture has come further revision of the earlier theory regarding the pliability of man in meeting his cultural demands. New knowledge concerning the individual coming from the laboratories of the biologist and the clinics of the psychologist and the physician has made plainer the differences in personal characteristics that entail greater or less difficulty in making suitable sociocultural adaptations. Such differences in personal traits cover a wide range of proclivities, such as bodily structure, constitution, organ condition and function, temperament, intelligence, and growth rates, many of which doubtless have a hereditary basis. They also include variations that are in part the result of manifold conditioning experiences, such as differences in ability to tolerate frustrations and deprivations, to postpone satisfactions, to rely on compensations for defaults, and to endure prolonged, monotonous efforts and strains. Likewise, individuals in the same culture, and siblings in the same family, are seen to vary greatly in their manner of accepting the consequence of an act and, as a corollary, in their qualifications for making commitments and assuming responsibilities involved in group life. Of no slight import, also, are variations in ability to make discriminations and to draw inferences that are pertinent to personal adaptations. An

[1] Representative writings include: Dollard, John, "Culture, Society, Impulse and Socialization," 1939; Ford, C. S., "Society, Culture, and the Human Organism," 1939; Gillin, John, "Personality Formation from the Comparative Cultural Point of View," 1948; Herskovits, M. J., "Culture and the Individual," 1948; Kardiner, Abram, *The Individual and His Society*, 1939; Idem, *The Psychological Frontiers of Society*, 1945; Kluckhohn, Clyde, and O. H. Mowrer, "Culture and Personality," 1944; Linton, Ralph, *Cultural Background of Personality*, 1945; *Idem*, "Culture, Society, and the Individual," 1938; Mead, Margaret, *Growing Up in New Guinea*, 1930; Meggers, B. J., "Recent Trends in American Ethnology," 1946; Opler, M. E., *An Apache Life-Way*, 1941; Warner, W. L., "The Society, the Individual, and His Mental Disorders," 1937.

indeterminate number and degree of these differences are deeply rooted in biological endowments and, although subject to cultural molding, are never quite made over.

Social Science Focus on the Individual

As a correlative to the new functional approach in cultural analysis *in situ*, there has also arisen in recent years a strong interest in the individual as a person and the reciprocal relationships that tie him in with the culture. The processes by which he is converted from a biological entity into a social being, and the stresses and strains that are thereby entailed for him, have come in for concentrated study. Thus, for further understanding of culture itself and for the social processes that underlie it, many scientists from various disciplines have turned to the individual and his experiences within the cultural framework. The life history[1] of a particular person has been viewed as a prism through which are reflected many significant facets of his society and his culture. These extensive personal documents now help to reveal how individuals are groomed and fitted into culturally defined stations and forced to fulfill their social roles, and they often can show at what price these adaptations are made.

The first extensive use of life-history materials for the study of sociocultural dynamics was made by the sociologists W. I. Thomas and Florian Znaniecki in their monumental work[2] *The*

[1] For assessments of the standards, techniques, and significance of life-history studies, consult: Allport, G. W., *The Use of Personal Documents in Psychological Science*, 1942; Cartwright, Dorwin, and J. R. P. French, Jr., "The Reliability of Life-History Studies," 1939; Cottrell, L. S., Jr., "The Case-Study Method in Prediction," 1941; Dollard, John, *Criteria for the Life History*, 1935; Gottschalk, L. R., Clyde Kluckhohn, and Robert Angell, *The Use of Personal Documents in History, Anthropology and Sociology*, 1945.

For examples of life histories of persons in primitive societies, see: Dyk, Walter, editor, *Son of Old Man Hat*, 1938; Idem, *Old Mexican, Navaho Indian:* A Navaho Autobiography, 1947; Ford, C. S., *Smoke from Their Fires*, 1941; Landes, Ruth, *The Ojibwa Woman*, 1938; Leighton, A. H., and D. C. Leighton, *Gregorio, the Hand-Trembler*, 1949; Radin, Paul, *Crashing Thunder*, 1926; Reyher, R. H., *Zulu Woman*, 1948; Simmons, L. W., editor, *Sun Chief:* The Autobiography of a Hopi Indian, 1942. See also, in connection with the last named, Aberle, D. F., *The Psychological Analysis of a Hopi Life History*, 1951.

[2] See also Blumer, Herbert, *An Appraisal of Thomas and Znaniecki's "The Polish Peasant in Europe and America,"* 1939.

Polish Peasant in the United States, published in five volumes during 1918–1920. Since then, personal documents have become an established means of gaining knowledge of the processes of social and personal disorganization, especially among the foreign-born, in our large modern urban centers. Similar materials have become standard data for studying the predicaments in which individuals find themselves as a result of rapid social changes, when they move from one culture to another, or from one social class or subculture to another, and when they are caught in cultural cross-currents that impinge upon them. In the light of such information, and our growing awareness of individual differences that are constitutional or acquired, it becomes easier to see how difficult it may be for certain persons to re-adapt, chameleon-like, to the changing social demands. It is not surprising, therefore, that some of these forces have been found to take a toll in the form of illness.

The "culture-personality" studies, based on personal documents have challenged students of the behavioral sciences to collaborate with clinicians. There is thus a growing body of literature that deals with the way a particular person learns to select his goals, fulfill his roles,[1] and fit his life into the existing

[1] Ackerman, N. W., "'Social Role' and Total Personality," 1951; Barnouw, Victor, *Acculturation and Personality Changes Among the Wisconsin Chippewa*, 1950; Bateson, Gregory, "Cultural Determinants of Personality," 1944; Bennett, J. W., "Culture Change and Personality in a Rural Society," 1944; Billig, Otto, John Gillin, and William Davidson, "Aspects of Personality and Culture in a Guatemalan Community," 1947–1948; Dai, Bingham, "Personality Problems in Chinese Culture," 1941; Devereux, George, "Mohave Culture and Personality," 1939; *Idem*, "Areal Culture Pattern and Areal Basic Personality," 1951; Gillin, John, "Personality in Preliterate Societies," 1939; Goldfrank, E. S., "Socialization, Personality, and the Structure of Pueblo Society," 1945; Goldhamer, Herbert, "Recent Development in Personality Studies," 1948; Kardiner, Abram, "The Concept of Basic Personality Structure as an Operational Tool in the Social Sciences," 1945; Linton, Ralph, "Problems of Status Personality," 1949; Mead, Margaret, "The Use of Primitive Material in the Study of Personality," 1935; *Idem*, "The Implications of Culture Change for Personality Development," 1947; Plant, J. S., *Personality and the Cultural Pattern*, 1937; Sapir, Edward, "The Emergence of the Concept of Personality in the Study of Cultures," 1934; Thomas, W. I., "The Configurations of Personality," 1928; Underwood, F. W., and Irma Honigmann, "A Comparison of Socialization and Personality in Two Simple Societies," 1947; Woodard, J. W., "The Relation of Personality Structure to the Structure of Culture," 1938.

social matrix. It attempts to show step by step how particular factors and forces within a sociocultural system shape the personal characteristics of the individual and affect his reactions to critical situations along the life course. In the case of small primitive groups, it has been possible to show how cultural influences have developed basically similar "modal" personalities in particular societies, and to draw distinctions between general manifestations of personality from society to society. In the more complex modern societies the further influence of class factors, subcultural groupings, and differentiated social roles upon personal adaptations to social demands and stress has been demonstrated.[1]

As a consequence of this work, we are now able to recognize, and we show considerable interest in, two especially important areas of socially determined stress in life situations. The first of these is the socialization processes by which the individual as a biological creature with limited endowments is forced into roles assigned to him by society and pressed into the mold of its culture. These "bringing-up" processes may exert considerable force upon him and condition him to later difficulties.[2] In the second place, as we shall show later, stress may also result from frictions produced by the various, and sometimes in-

[1] Centers, Richard, *The Psychology of Social Classes*, 1949; Davis, Kingsley, and W. E. Moore, "Some Principles of Stratification," 1945; Davis, Allison, and R. J. Havighurst, *Father of the Man*, 1947; Goldschmidt, W. R., "Social Class in America," 1950; Harvey, O. J., "An Experimental Approach to the Study of Status Relations in Informal Groups," 1953; Hetzler, S. A., "An Investigation of the Distinctiveness of Social Classes," 1953; Hollingshead, A. B., "Trends in Social Stratification," 1952; Idem, *Elmtown's Youth*, 1949; *Idem*, "The Concept of Social Control," 1941; *Idem*, "Selected Characteristics of Classes in a Middle Western Community," 1947; Hughes, E. C., "Dilemma and Contradictions of Status," 1945; Lewin, Kurt, *Resolving Social Conflicts*, 1948; Warner, W. L., Marchia Meeker, and Kenneth Eells, *Social Class in America*, 1949.

[2] Bossard, J. H. S., *The Sociology of Child Development*, 1948; Davis, Allison, and John Dollard, *Children of Bondage*, 1940; Dennis, Wayne, *The Hopi Child*, 1940; *Idem*, "The Socialization of the Hopi Child," 1941; Erikson, E. H., *Childhood and Society*, 1950; Fleming, C. M., *Adolescence*, 1949; Josselyn, I. M., *Psychosocial Development of Children*, 1948; Leighton, D. C., and Clyde Kluckhohn, *Children of the People*, 1947; Mead, Margaret, and F. C. Macgregor, *Growth and Culture*, 1951; Plant, J. S., *The Envelope*, 1950; Pollak, Otto, and Yonata Feldman, "Culture and Culture Conflict in Psychotherapy," 1952.

compatible, roles an individual has to play in his society, and by other "stress-traps" in his culture, such as the conflicting norms and codes that spring from cross-currents within the social milieu.

Insights into these areas have been achieved already by varied social science or related disciplines. Much of our knowledge concerning the mechanisms involved in the socialization processes has come from the researches carried on within the laboratory of the experimental psychologists. There it is shown that socialization or acculturation conforms basically to the principles of the laboratory learning processes, but qualified by other significant factors difficult to control in the laboratory, as, for example, the conscious and unconscious conditioning carried on by variable systems of reward and punishments with which the individual is surrounded throughout his life. If this process is successful, the individual learns to conform to the mandates of his culture, to relate himself appropriately to his fellows, and at the same time to find adequate expression or satisfaction of his chief impulses and needs.[1] It is apparent, however, that this process is a delicate one and that many circumstances may prejudice a person's chance for successful adaptations on both the social and biological levels.

As to how these molding forces affect the mental and emotional make-up of the individual, or his personality, important insights can be found in the field of psychiatry and abnormal psychology. Here are dramatic data that show, at least in part,

[1] Benedek, Therese, *Insight and Personality Adjustment*, 1946; Benedict, Ruth, "Continuities and Discontinuities in Cultural Conditioning," 1938; Coutu, Walter, *Emergent Human Nature*, 1949; Gillin, John, "Acquired Drives in Culture Contact," 1942; Hovland, C. I., I. L. Janis, and H. H. Kelley, *Communication and Persuasion*, 1953; Kahn, Eugen, and L. W. Simmons, "Problems of Middle Age," 1939; Klineberg, Otto, "A Science of National Character," 1944; Mowrer, O. H., *Learning Theory and Personality Dynamics*, 1950; Pollak, Otto, *Social Adjustment in Old Age*, 1948; Ruesch, Jurgen, Annemarie Jacobson, and M. B. Loeb, *Acculturation and Illness*, 1948; Saul, L. J., *Emotional Maturity*, 1947; Simmons, L. W., *The Role of the Aged in Primitive Society*, 1945; *Idem*, "The Dynamic Psychology of the Group and the Shaping of Individual Behavior," 1950; *Idem*, "A Prospectus for Field-Research in the Position and Treatment of the Aged in Primitive and Other Societies," 1945.

the heavy demands society makes upon the organisms and how such individuals resort to all kinds of devices and strategies in order to evade or cope with the stresses engendered. Free association of ideas, dream analysis, the utilization of physician-patient relationships, and techniques for acting out long-standing aggressive behavior patterns provide further evidence of the repressed and subsequently explosive or distorting elements in the socialization processes, especially in family settings. They show how pressing natural impulses or magnified life goals when denied or frustrated beyond tolerance, especially during the formative years, may have lasting effects upon the individual, resulting in the mobilization and habituation of avoidance behavior and defensive attitudes and activities that intensify disharmony and multiply the maladaptations.[1]

Anthropologists, as indicated above, have demonstrated the vast range of cultural dictates, the contextual relevance as well as the comparative relativity of cultural phenomena for personal adaptations, and the functional continuities both in specific social settings and in the integration of personality "types" or "modes" of response. Malinowski, for example, pointed out, perhaps first and foremost, that interpersonal conflicts and stresses associated with parent-child relationships depend largely upon the kinds of pressures imposed upon the individual by the social structure and the family configuration, and he showed how these may vary greatly from culture to culture.[2] As a result of such data and interpretations from many sources, it is now reasonable to think in terms of the

[1] Anderson, V. V., *Psychiatry in Industry*, 1929; Devereux, George, "Psychiatry and Anthropology," 1952; Frank, L. K., *Society as the Patient*, 1948; Greenacre, Phyllis, *Trauma, Growth, and Personality*, 1952; Hollingshead, A. B., and F. C. Redlich, "Social Stratification and Psychiatric Disorders," 1953; Horney, Karen, *The Neurotic Personality of Our Time*, 1937; Kroeber, A. L., "Psychosis or Social Sanction," 1940; Sapir, Edward, "Cultural Anthropology and Psychiatry," 1932; Weinberg, S. K., *Society and Personality Disorders*, 1952.

[2] Malinowski, Bronislaw, *Sex and Repression in Savage Society*, 1927; Idem, *The Father in Primitive Psychology*, 1927.

"neurotic personality" that is relevant to a specified sociocultural setting, and with qualifications based on time and place.

Instead of showing special concern for the broad-gauge contrasts between very different and more or less homogeneous primitive cultures of a worldwide variety, the sociologists have been making major contributions by concentrating their attention on our contemporary, so-called civilized, and very heterogeneous sociocultural systems of group life. They, too, have attempted to work largely within the broad cultural frame of reference. Owing, however, to the vast complexities of modern social life, they have endeavored to subdivide the social milieu into subcultural areas and to delineate and assess differences therein that have a significant bearing upon individual and group adaptations. Thus, for example, they have been concerned with immigrant in contrast to native cultural backgrounds, with one sociogeographic area as compared with another within the same national unit, with rural versus urban social determinants, or with slum areas in contrast to developed sections in the same city.

They have also shown great interest in contrasts between the dynamics involved in one socioeconomic class or status group and that of another within the same population, and with differences arising from contrasting types of family structures and functions. Sometimes these subdivisions are split up into very fine points of reference, such as degrees in formal education. So, in substance, and with blurred zones of distinction between the fields to be sure, the sociologists have attempted to refine and particularize the cultural approach, perhaps applying their skills in some areas with greater precision, for they utilize procedures of sampling and statistical validation that are less frequently used in the anthropological approach. They have specialized mainly in smaller and smaller subdivisions of what may be regarded as a single over-all cultural milieu, our own contemporary, heterogeneous, and rapidly changing society. Therefore, their studies for practical use are often of more immediate relevance.[1]

In addition to subdivisions of the cultural frame of reference, the sociologists are much concerned with the observable details and processes involved in interpersonal and group relationships within settings of organized or structured associations under recognized and sanctioned position and role assignments. Systematic attempts are made to document and analyze these relationships, to discover the repetitive regularities in operation, and to generalize with descriptive and predictive formulations.[2]

Here again, the detailed and comprehensive documentation of individual personal experience within these group processes has become very highly prized; particularly is this so whenever equally full documentation can be secured on the several key participants in a given situation or series of situations under study. Such a grouping of related personal documents promises to reveal new insights into the dynamics of interpersonal and group relationships when they can be studied in a comparative context. The total portrayal of a selected series of such documents centered within a given social unit, such as a family, clinic, workshop, or larger institutionalized subgroup context, provides interlocking data for verification and generalization. When the unit is large, compromises have to be made, of course, and the research specialist resorts to tech-

[1] Caplow, Theodore, and R. E. Forman, "Neighborhood Interaction in a Homogeneous Community," 1950; Cottrell, L. S., Jr., "The Adjustment of the Individual to His Age and Sex Roles," 1942; *Idem*, "The Analysis of Situational Fields in Social Psychology," 1942; Davie, M. R., "The Patterns of Urban Growth," 1937; Hetzler, S. A., "An Investigation of the Distinctiveness of Social Classes," 1953; Hollingshead, A. B., "A Re-examination of Ecological Theory," 1947; Mukherjee, Ramkrishna, "The Economic Structure and Social Life in Six Villages of Bengal," 1949; Myers, J. K., "Assimilation to the Ecological and Social Systems of a Community," 1950; Parsons, Talcott, "Age and Sex in the Social Structure of the United States," 1942; Robinson, W. S., "Ecological Correlations and the Behavior of Individuals," 1950; Shils, E. A., *The Present State of American Sociology*, 1948; Warner, W. L., and P. S. Lunt, *The Social Life of a Modern Community*, 1941; West, James, *Plainville, U. S. A.*, 1945; Whyte, W. F., *Street Corner Society*, 1943.

[2] Homans, G. C., *The Human Group*, 1950.

niques of sampling along with briefer and more sharply focused schedules of inquiry, such as questionnaires, formalized interviews, periodic observations, and so on. But the chief objective remains one of searching for the dependable variables that produce whatever regularities may be discerned in the social phenomena.

From various social science approaches, the individual has become the center of attention. He is now, in much more than a figurative sense, the *bug* on the social science pin. It is recognized that stamped upon his personality, built into his reaction patterns, and sometimes deeply embedded in his bodily structures are the impact of his culture and the scars of his society, inflicted as a consequence of his particular place in life. Moreover, his personal history, more than anything else we can call upon, reveals the conflicts and stresses, the processes of conditioning by achievements and defeats, and some of the dynamics that have gone into the shaping of his adaptations to his total milieu. As a "whole person," the individual has, indeed, come into his own for scientific study.

Thus, it has now become almost axiomatic that adequate understanding of any individual, either as a functioning biological organism or as a responding person, is possible only when available information portrays and regards, indeed contemplates, him as a member of a specified group and as a product of that group's culture. Reciprocally, it is recognized now by many social scientists that an effective way of probing into the real significance of a given cultural milieu is to investigate and scrutinize the pressures and limitations that it exerts upon specific individuals and as reflected in their life histories.

Perhaps it will never be possible completely to unravel the relationships of biology and sociology, of bodily and social demands, or of the reflexes and the folkways, in the case record of any particular person. The new perspective, however, promises to provide further significant knowledge for a science of man. It may also provide some new insights and potential controls for the prevention and treatment of man's diseases.

THE ROLE OF PERSPECTIVES IN MEDICAL CARE AND SOME PROBLEMS IN MEDICOSOCIAL CONVERGENCE

It thus becomes apparent that there are varied perspectives from which to view the problems of disease and its control. Some may look at illness and its possible prevention or treatment within a limited field, as through a microscope. Others may consider the same questions with broader horizons, as though macroscopically. Between the two extremes the range varies, providing anything from pinpoint to panoramic pictures. Irrespective of viewpoint, however, all who are concerned with the problems of health generally share one common interest, a sharper perception of a *functional unit* in illness that will make the facts about the disease more intelligible and its course more manageable.

However we may look at the problem, from broad or narrow range, progress in the health field depends upon these clearer conceptions of the identifiable functional units that will provide greater knowledge and better controls. The more clearly the target for action can be seen, the better will be the score of direct hits; and clarity of perception, socially and medically speaking, depends largely upon the skill and ability to apply the correct perspectives at the appropriate time. Not infrequently a new slant on a well-known issue marks another milestone in medicine. Indeed, the search for another perspective that will bring into focus and clarify the next most manageable functional unit in the control of an illness constitutes, in a sense, the perennial quest for the Holy Grail in medicine.

Some examples of rewarding perspectives that have come out of the physical and medical sciences are: the concepts of organic lesions and defects; focus on cell composition and growth; the discovery and identification of invading agents;

recognition of systems of organs functioning as units; consideration of the whole body as the adaptive unit in which all organs and systems of organs are interrelated; and, more recently, scientific concern for the patient as a goal-directed person, whose adjustments and disease are patterned by his previous experiences and responses.

Reversing the line of progression, and reviewing some of the potential perspectives growing out of the social sciences, we have, first, the concepts of the over-all cultural unit, the tribe, state, or nation operating as a whole; the ethnic or racial subgroups within the society; the socioeconomic classes; the occupational categories; the community and neighborhood, and the medical institution itself; and, finally, the family, the smallest but certainly not the least important social unit for coping with disease.

There is thus a range of potential perspectives on the control of disease that runs from organ or even cell to community, country, or total cultural unit; each with promise of new leads in medical progress. Some gains have been made by exploring the separate perspectives, and others come through an integration of the varied viewpoints. But as we move in our thinking from the micro- to the macroscopical perspectives, vagueness develops and gaps appear progressively in the formulations and with respect to scientific controls in prevention and treatment. Actual confusion can arise, moreover, at the borderlines of integration between the various perspectives, and a formidable cleavage may all but divide the theoretical formulations of the biological components on the one side and the sociological factors on the other, even though they are always merged and mixed in the life of the patient.

As one moves "up" from cell or organ to the "whole body" on the biological side and "down" from the cultural unit, nation, tribe, or community to the family on the sociological side, the break in linkage is sharpest between the body as the largest biological unit and the family as the smallest sociological unit. The whole body is seen adapting to disease and the family coping with illness. In between have arisen new concepts of the person, or personality, as the logical linkage of the biological and sociological dynamics. Since the conceptual gap between the whole body and the family unit appears to be the most critical cleft in a unified biosocial perspective on disease and its dynamics, the role of personality in disease deserves special attention and systematic exploration.

There is, of course, some recognized bridging of biology and sociology in the idea of hereditary transmission of certain disabilities or susceptibility to them. Other biosocial tie-ins are apparent as, for example, in the communication of infectious diseases through social contacts, occupational hazards, the occurrence of accidents through lapses in social control, and the existence of physical privations, such as insufficient food, shelter, or medical care, as a consequence of social neglect or mismanagement. Some of these resulting ailments may even be characterized as "social diseases." Biosocial linkage is also assumed in the recognized obligations of a community or family toward its sick, the aged, and otherwise incapacitated members; and social medicine has become meaningful. Preventive and treatment policies and programs involve sociological factors and principles in both the planning and execution of good medical care.[1]

[1] Examples of the broadening approach to medical problems are seen in such writings as: Ashley-Montague, Francis, "The Sociobiology of Man," 1940; Clausen, J. A., "Social Science Research in the National Mental Health Program," 1950; Galdston, Iago, "Biodynamic Medicine Versus Psychosomatic Medicine," 1944; *Idem*, editor, *Social Medicine*, 1949; *Idem*, "Social Medicine and the Epidemic Constitution," 1951; *Idem*, "The Implications of Recent Advances in Medicine for Public Health," 1952; Hall, Oswald, "Sociological Research in the Field of Medicine," 1951; Leavell, H. R., "Contributions of the Social Sciences to the Solution of Health Problems," 1952; Mangus, A. R., and J. R. Seeley, *Mental Health Needs*, 1950; Milbank Memorial Fund, *Backgrounds of Social Medicine*, 1949; Morgan, C. T., *Physiological Psychology*, 1943; Roemer, M. I., "Relationship of Social Medicine to the Social Sciences," 1948; Rosen, G. "What Is Social Medicine?" 1947; *Idem*, "The Ideal of Social Medicine in America," 1949; Sand, René, *Health and Human Progress*, 1936; Idem, *The Advance to Social Medicine*, 1952; Smillie, W. G., "Medicine as a Social Instrument," 1952; Stern, B. J., *Society and Medical Progress*, 1941.

It is thus becoming more and more apparent that the individual's bodily economy is profoundly affected by his experience. This fact encourages systematic study of society and culture for medical purposes. Indeed, it may help us understand how personal goals, values, attitudes, and emotional states are built into life patterns of adjustment and how they become intervening variables in the experience of stress and disease.

CHAPTER 3

Society, Culture, and the Individual

WHEN CLINICIANS DELIBERATE in staff conferences on problems of health and illness, frequent reference is made to the phrase "the individual in his environment." This usage generally conveys a sobering realization of the many vital links between the organism and the environment. In effect, it helps to apply brakes to possibly unsound, or too narrowly gauged, speculations and procedures in therapy, for it implies some recognition of other elements, that is, social and personal, in the individual-environment picture. Hence, it testifies to that fine medical sense of responsibility and insight which so often counsels leaving certain maladjustments more or less as they are, rather than jeopardize the welfare of the patient in other ways.

Nevertheless, the individual-environment idea, however basic it may be, is too broad to be put to good use unless the important aspects of the relationship are particularized and attention is directed to the identifiable sets of variables on each side that may be pertinent and correlative. To view the individual simply as the organism, and the environment grossly as "anything and everything outside the skin of the patient," and to try to draw conclusions concerning the impact of the environment upon the patient or the capacity of the patient to cope with his environment is well-nigh futile. Failure to be specific may be as useless in the psychosocial, or what is regarded as the nonphysical, as in the physical areas of human adaptation. To lump together individual traits and environmental factors in the sociocultural areas of adaptation may prove to be no more effectual than to do the same thing with the physical. Specificity is required in both.[1]

It is, indeed, trite to emphasize the need for such specificity on the level of the organism's adaptations to its physical surroundings, for this is the accepted principle in both scientific and therapeutic endeavors. Among such procedures are the consideration of organic dysfunctions, invading organisms, differential medications, diets, temperatures, and countless other refinements in the checking of possible critical variables.

When it comes to consideration of social and personal relationships and their bearing on illness, however, even grossly equivalent methods can scarcely be found. Here, in contrast, formulations appear haphazard and casual, leading sometimes to the accumulation of vast amounts of social and cultural data about a patient with little knowledge of how to analyze or use them. Their relevance, nevertheless, is rarely doubted. Fewer and fewer illnesses are now regarded as completely free from personal and social complications that may alter their course. Even a broken leg may involve quite complex personal and social factors that influence recovery.

If, then, we are to seek a clear-cut formulation embracing both the physical and social scientific approaches in medicine, it is necessary to analyze the individual-environment concept much more closely and to endow it with more content and meaning.

The individual may be viewed, profitably, as adapting to life situations on three levels of integration between himself and his environment. He reacts as an *organism* in his physical surroundings, as a *group member* or agent in his society, and as a *person* or personality in his culture. Perhaps the critical categories may be diagramed to advantage as indicated on page 52.

[1] Chase, Stuart, *The Proper Study of Mankind*, 1948; Childe, V. G., *Social Evolution*, 1952; Clark, D. W., "The Social Environment as a Concern of Preventive Medicine," 1951; Frank, L. K., "Man's Multidimensional Environment," 1943; Idem, *Society as the Patient*, 1948; Freed, L. F., "Philosophy of Sociological Medicine," 1948; Kluckhohn, Clyde, *Mirror for Man*, 1949; Kroeber, A. L., "So-called Social Science," 1936; Malinowski, Bronislaw, *A Scientific Theory of Culture*, 1944.

Laying out the matter as an over-all approach to illness and medical care points up problems related to clarifying definitions, correlating identifiable elements, and formulating integrating principles. Such questions arise, for example, as to what is implied in the concept of agent or group member in contrast to organism; or in person or personality, in contradistinction to organism or agent? What is meant by the concept *society*, as something superimposed upon the physical environment; and how may the idea of culture differ from that

The Individual	acts in	His Environment
1. As an Organism	in its	Physical Habitat
2. As a Group Member	in his	Society
3. As a Person	in his	Culture

THREE LEVELS OF FUNCTION OF THE INDIVIDUAL

of society, which introduces still another important category of variables into the picture? Moreover, what components or mechanisms can be identified as continuities between the individual as an organism, a group agent, and a personality on the one hand, and what similar linkages can be identified between the physical environment, society, and culture on the other? What can be found that is tangible and measurable in the connecting relationships between the individual and his environment up and down the line, and how much of this can be seen as pertinent to understanding and coping with a patient in his life situation? Indeed, how may a situation and an interpersonal relationship be more clearly defined in such a landscape?

As in any rounded-out perspective, when subunits are once identified and understood in relation to one another, the disturbing dividing lines and apparent cleavages disappear and the parts merge into larger patterns of unity. But to know the parts and their interrelationships is indispensable to knowledge of the whole. Such unity in perspective is a distant, perhaps far distant, goal in medicosocial science, albeit not beyond practical approach. Long before it can be attained, however, much joint work remains to be done on the major segments of the whole. Chief of these for our immediate purpose is the task of defining the concepts of society and culture and integrating these concepts with those of the individual in his larger environment.

Society and Culture

From much observation in clinical conferences set up for the avowed purpose of clarifying problems of the dynamics in disease and planning courses of treatment, it would appear that the words "culture" and "society" are used interchangeably. Apparently clinicians find it easier to view the environment in dichotomous categories of the physical surroundings and the general sociocultural milieu. Probably this is to be expected and may have something in its favor, for no physician sees patients possessing a culture and surviving outside a society; and no anthropologist finds human beings surviving in societies without the benefits of a culture. For man, both society and culture are indispensable and thus they appear inseparable and, in many ways, synonymous. Why, then, attempt to perceive them separately, as each possessing independent variables?

The same question could be asked with respect to the physical and nonphysical (social or cultural) environments. Since both are indispensable in the life of a human being, why see them as two parts? The answer is a practical one. It helps us perceive and formulate the dynamics of the individual's behavior, and also to predict or control that behavior within limits.[1] For the same purpose, we subscribe conceptually to a trichotomous division of man's environment into the physical, societal, and cultural spheres. Such a formulation fits the facts more adequately, outlines the problems more clearly, provides a better classification of the variables, and affords a greater promise of prediction and control. This position calls for preliminary discussion of society and culture.

Society is concrete, above all. Its phenomena are easier to identify and objectify than are those of culture. Anyone in doubt about the realities of societal factors needs only to withdraw as completely as possible from group life to discover how many of his goals, activities, and satisfactions depend upon relationships with others. Or he may deviate from his accustomed behavior and disrupt the affairs of his fellows in their established functions within the social system and thereby experience the impact of their separate or combined efforts to curb or punish him. Sometimes all a person has to do in order to sense sharply the forces in society is to let down his guards, stop defending his interests, and lay himself open to the exploitations and aggressions of others. Even an attempt just to "go about his own business" may reveal how pressing can become the demands to "play his part" in the joint interests and activities of varied group memberships. Or, if he neglects certain duties ascribed to him, he will soon find how sure and pointed can be the penalties for his failure to "fit in." In such ways the realities of society keep the individual in line, and they are at all times verifiable.

[1] The differences involved in the concepts of society and culture are summarized in Nadel, S. F., *The Foundations of Social Anthropology*, 1951. See also Herskovits, M. J., *Man and His Works*, 1948; Hiller, E. T., *Social Relations and Structure*, 1947; Linton, Ralph, *The Study of Man*, 1936; Stern, B. J., "Concerning the Distinction Between the Social and the Cultural," 1929; Steward, J. H., "Levels of Sociocultural Integration," 1951.

Indeed, a person may become vividly aware of the presence of society's forces through its functionaries who inspect and pass upon his performance, or lack of it, at every turn. Their joint behavior in forcing action on his part is also obvious; and this "big stick," in the form of organized group pressure, plays a more decisive and dramatic role in settling issues and getting results than do the deliberations concerning values and virtues (the justified "rights and wrongs" and the appropriate "ways and means") that constitute culture. Thus, in any social situation, the pushes and pulls of society's "pressure personnel" appear more immediately real and urgent than are the background cultural patterns of norms and rules that have become more or less idealized. For man, to be sure, culture sets the stage, ascribes the parts, and defines the terms whereby society's drama is enacted. It is, however, the membership of the society that plays out the assigned parts in the drama, adds the teeth to the culture, and puts the bite on every participating member. Society is deeply rooted and reified in the operations and enforcements of organized group life.[1]

A group of individuals may or may not form a society. In simplest terms, a society is an organization of member agents. Thus, a society always arises out of groups, but it is something more than a mere aggregation. The outstanding characteristic of society is a *system*—a system of membership positions and interacting relationships that effect certain regularities in the adaptive behavior of the individuals within the organized group. In a society the several organisms, or member agents, take their places in some observable relationship to one another and interact in a more or less repetitive and predictable

[1] For representative material on this subject, see: Allport, G. W., *The ABC's of Scapegoating*, 1948; Allport, G. W., and L. J. Postman, *The Psychology of Rumor*, 1947; Hollingshead, A. B., "The Concept of Social Control," 1941; Kahn, Eugen, and L. W. Simmons, "Problems of Middle Age," 1939; Lewin, Kurt, *Resolving Social Conflicts*, 1948; Lewin, Kurt, and others; "Patterns of Aggressive Behavior in Experimentally Created Social Climates," 1939; Mead, G. H., *Mind, Self and Society*, 1934; Merton, R. K., *Mass Persuasion*, 1946; Murphy, Gardner, and Rensis Likert, *Public Opinion and the Individual*, 1938.

manner. The recurring pattern is referred to as a structured group relationship.[1]

In many of the insect and animal species these structured positions and interactions are inborn. The organized behavior of ants and bees provides good examples of structured systems that are relatively invariable. In human societies the systems of patterned positions and responses are acquired primarily through learning, although chiefly unconsciously, and are known as conditioning or acculturation.[2] They are variable and are largely culturally prescribed. The most important point to note here is that there are countless subhuman societies existing *free from culture*. They are sometimes remarkably complex and structured, nevertheless, and a member's position and behavior in them are far more predictable than are those of an individual in a human society. The propensities for the structured relationships can be said to be rooted in the germ plasm and transmitted by heredity. Knowledge of these cultureless societies is helpful in clarifying the concept of society in general and in portraying these noncultural, societal factors as actual independent, and critical variables in the life of an individual.[3]

[1] Childe, V. G., *Social Evolution*, 1952; Herskovits, M. J., "Social Organization," 1948; Hertzler, J. O., *Social Institutions*, 1946; Lévi-Strauss, Claude, "Social Structure," 1953; Lowie, R. H., *Social Organization*, 1948; MacIver, R. M., *Society*, 1937; Merton, R. K., *Social Theory and Social Structure*, 1949; Murdock, G. P., *Social Structure*, 1949; Parsons, Talcott, *The Social System*, 1951; Radcliffe-Brown, A. R., *Structure and Function in Primitive Society*, 1952.

[2] Hallowell, A. I., "Sociopsychological Aspects of Acculturation," 1945; Hilgard, E. R., *Theories of Learning*, 1948; Miller, N. E., and John Dollard, *Social Learning and Imitation*, 1941; Opler, M. E., "Cultural Alternatives and Educational Theory," 1947; Thurnwald, Richard, "The Psychology of Acculturation," 1932; Whiting, J. W. H., *Becoming a Kwoma*, 1941.

[3] Allee, W. C., *The Social Life of Animals*, 1938; Carpenter, C. R., "A Field Study of the Behavior and Social Relations of Howling Monkeys," 1934; *Idem*, "Characteristics of Social Behavior in Non-human Primates," 1942; Emerson, A. E., "Basic Comparisons of Human and Insect Societies," 1942; James, W. T., "Social Organization Among Dogs of Different Temperaments," 1951; Krogman, W. M., "The Man-Apes of South Africa," 1948; Kropotkin, P. A., *Mutual Aid:* A Factor of Evolution, 1916; Schjelderup-Ebbe, Thorleif, "Social Behavior of Birds," 1935; Yerkes, R. M., *Chimpanzees*, 1943; Yerkes, R. M., and A. W. Yerkes, "Social Behavior in Infrahuman Primates," 1935; Zuckerman, Solly, *The Social Life of Monkeys and Apes*, 1932.

Wheeler[1] shows clearly and dramatically the structured systems of relationships in behavior whereby the fate of each individual in certain societies is interlocked with that of the other members of the group. Thus, the life of ants and bees is largely social, that is, distinctly dependent upon the structured relationships with their fellow insects, but it is not a product of culture.

Culture-determined human societies are very different from somatic-determined insect societies, although both have organization with a system of membership positions and responses that are repetitive and predictable within measurable limits. It is in the analysis of *organization* that the concept of societies of all types takes on its special significance for our purpose. Organization, or what is now called *social structure*, is the touchstone of all societies.[2]

In the phenomena of society, human and nonhuman, culture-bearing and culture-free, are certain other common denominators, inherent in organization, that further define and clarify the concept. *Individual differences*, related to capacity, position, and performance, may be discerned within any organized or structured group membership. These may be based on size, weight, strength, age, sex, bodily structure, aptitude, habit, skill, or other distinctions. Some of these permit certain individuals to dominate others in the system; and this coercive relationship, which can and usually does arise, has been

[1] Wheeler, W. M., *Social Life Among the Insects*, 1928.

[2] For additional references on human social organization, see: Bain, Read, "Action Research and Group Dynamics," 1951; Bales, R. F., *Interaction Process Analysis*, 1950; Bendix, Reinhard, and S. M. Lipset, editors, *Class, Status and Power*, 1953; Bogardus, E. S., "Social Distance and Its Origins," 1925; *Idem*, "Social Distance: A Measuring Stick," 1926; Brown, G. G., and J. H. Barnett, "Social Organization and Social Structure," 1942; Brown, J. F., *Psychology and the Social Order*, 1936; Chapin, F. S., *The Measurement of Social Status by Use of the Social Status Scale*, 1933; *Idem*, "Latent Culture Patterns of the Unseen World of Social Reality," 1934; Davis, Kingsley, *Human Society*, 1949; Eggan, F. R., *Social Organization of the Western Pueblos*, 1950; Lowie, R. H., *Social Organization*, 1948; MacIver, R. M., *Community*, 1931; Mills, T. M., "Power Relations in Three-Person Groups," 1953; Ogburn, W. F., *Social Change*, rev. 1950; Roberts, J. M., *Three Navaho Households*, 1952; Ruesch, Jurgen, and Gregory Bateson, *Communication:* The Social Matrix of Psychiatry, 1951.

dubbed the "pecking order." Fowls, let loose in a coop, for example, soon begin to participate in an adaptive relationship to one another in which some dominate and others submit.[1] This ordering of relationships can occur within, or independent of, a cultural milieu of norms and pressures.

These same individual differences, innate or acquired, are also the source of specialization in function and division of labor. All societies, with or without culture, demonstrate this in some measure. In insect societies it is carried to fantastic limits, even though instinct-determined. In other societies the instinctive patterns of behavior are far more flexible and specialization may be less specific. Specialization may be to some extent voluntary, resulting from purposeful learning of a trade or profession, for example, or it may be largely coercive, imposed by group members in positions of dominance or by the economic system itself. Thus, for instance, the Chinese coolie has had little opportunity to seek other fields regardless of his qualifications. Then, again, specialization of function may be largely traditional, or passed down from father to son in a more or less stable society, as in the case of the French peasant farmer. Whatever the origin—inborn or learned and voluntary or coercive—these interactive positions and repetitive behavior in the social structure provide certain reciprocal and mutual benefits to the membership. They serve to sustain the group that in turn sustains the group members.[2]

In any social system individual differences that produce specialization or are produced by specialization set up relationships of subordination and superordination and provide the circumstances and the components for *cooperation*. This may be foreign to the common conception of the word in which the willing and purposeful teamwork of more or less equal members is usually implied. But in analysis of societal processes,

[1] Schjelderup-Ebbe, Thorleif, "Social Behavior of Birds," 1935.

[2] See Sumner, W. G., and A. G. Keller, *The Science of Society*, 1927, vol. 1, pp. 3–43.

mechanisms that provide some orderly way of sustaining the life of the group and prevent a general "free-for-all," even if they may not be in the best interest of each individual, must be termed "cooperative." Many forms of cooperation are actually "antagonistic cooperation," representing a conflict of interests between members although fulfilling common goals for the group.

A diagram may make these basic characteristics of the societal elements and relationships easier to understand. It shows

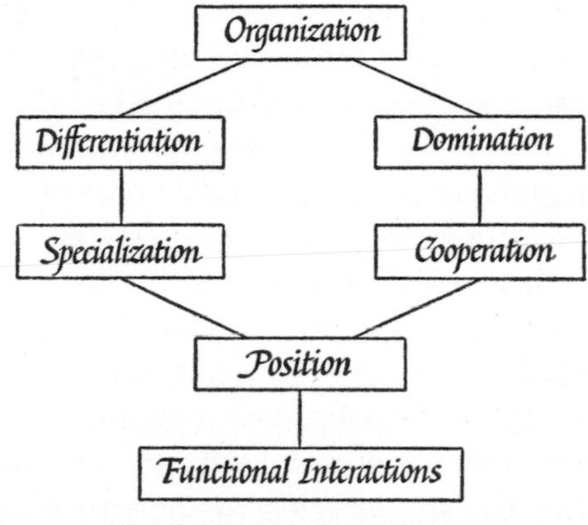

STRUCTURE OF SOCIETY

how differentiation and specialization on the one hand, and domination and cooperation on the other, establish positions or stations for all members of society. These lead to interactions between them that meet the interests of society and at the same time provide a degree of security for the individual by establishing a niche for him in the social structure and ascribing to him certain roles or duties.

Structured social life, which serves as the foundation of society, thus relies upon stabilized, repetitive, and sequential interactions between its members that correspond to the positions they hold in the system or in its subdivisions. These station-role relationships[1] of the membership within the system are interlocked in ways that make the behavior of a particular member neither independent nor passive. Such a group agent *belongs* to the system, has a place to fill, a function to perform, or a role to play, and a vital stake in the organized group unit. Thus, a member is not a free agent. His behavior is channeled by the system and is predictable within measurable degrees on the basis of the linked relationships. He may be forced to conform to system-determined demands even at the expense of individual needs and in the face of physical dangers.

A synoptic sketch of the most important positional categories that an individual's associates may occupy with respect to him are, first, the twofold alignments based on the *ingroup* and *outgroup*.[2] The members of any group, whether family, clan, college, fraternity, religious affiliation, tribe, or nationality, are bound together by ingroup interests, some of which are paramount to those of all nonmembers, who constitute outgroupers. In the second place, and within the organized ingroup, the relationships are generally regarded as at least threefold with respect to positional categories that relate to the individual. The rankings of one's fellows in relation to oneself are roughly defined as *surrogates* or superordinates, *peers* or equals, and *subordinates*.[3] These are the stationed agents of society in designated positions who react with or act upon the particular individual under consideration. Their relationships to him fall within a range of influence that may run from extremes of domination to abject submission. The surrogates exercise their power of domination by means of sanctions, and the subordinates, reciprocally, acquiesce. What may be called "antagonistic cooperation" operates up and down the line of relationships with the nearest approach to mutual and volun-

[1] Linton, Ralph, *The Study of Man*, 1936, pp. 113–131.

[2] Sumner, W. G., and A. G. Keller, *The Science of Society*, 1927, vol. 1. See also Index, "Ingroup and outgroup."

[3] Mead, Margaret, "Social Change and the Cultural Surrogates," 1940.

tary cooperation appearing between the individual and his peers, probably because of a wider range of equal powers and common interests.

The actions and reactions of these fellow-group agents, from their stations and with their prerogatives, produce pressures upon the individual. A combination of these can be overwhelming. These interactive relationships constitute the vital societal elements with which an individual must cope and upon which he must rely; first, in his initial helplessness and later on in life in his recurrent intervals of dependence, and, indeed, even in periods of stability and achievement. Thus, the very relationships that sustain him also threaten him and become highly surcharged for him with attitudes of confidence or fear, love or hate, and tendencies to approach or withdraw, to dominate or submit, and many other combinations in social relationships. Particular situations become repetitive and persistent, setting up recurrent stresses that may be manifest in the physiological processes. And it is probably trite to emphasize that the cumulative effect of such tensions and physically taxing responses, even though subtle and hidden, can wear down and waste away the resources of the individual, and sometimes even wreck the organism.

In short, man is uniquely a societal creature who through a long period of development has become dependent for his very existence upon the system-determined aids, supports, and reinforcements of fellow members of his "ingroups." He lives so much within these structured, repetitive, and dependent relationships, and in such concern about fellow expectations of him, that perhaps the greatest threat of all is his doubt about his ability to live the life of a man. He is threatened by those very forces in society upon which he is dependent for nourishment and life. He must be a part of the system and yet he is driven to fulfill his own proclivities; and because of his sensitive equipment, he is often pulled different ways at one time. These threats and conflicts are omnipresent, and constitute for him, above all organisms, a large portion of the stresses and strains to which he is exposed.

Society thus becomes for us a significant concept. It helps to make clear the vast network of relationships and compulsions that propel, direct, and constrain man's individual efforts but that bear forcefully upon his strongest and most intimate feelings about himself, reinforcing his personal satisfactions, yet increasing the tensions occasioned by frustration or failure in the achievement of his goals.

Yet, man is more than a social animal; he is also a culture-bearing creature. He and he alone has culture and some capacity to create and change it; and from these facts spring many of his differences from other forms of life, as well as the nature of many of his conflicts and stresses. Granting man's biological capacities and limitations, and his life in groups, his culture more than anything else explains his uniqueness in distinguishing him from other creatures.

In effect, man as a tribal member has been able to build for himself another milieu, or dimension of the environment, within which and by means of which he comes to terms with life situations. The concept of culture, superimposed upon that of society, provides a third identifiable and definable category of environmental variables, or, in another sense, a third level of adjustment that is difficult to separate from the societal level but that is not to be found, except perhaps in the most vestigial forms, in the adaptations of any other species.

What is this phenomenon called "culture," without which man apparently cannot live and that, for all practical purposes, puts a gulf between him and other creatures? Can we define it and formulate its importance in human life in such manner as to apprehend and assess its place in the trichotomy of environmental factors that impinge upon the individual?

Our special knowledge of culture and its relation to personal adaptations is recent. It can be claimed that the "discovery of culture," especially its significance for the individual both as an organism and as a person, is one of the outstanding achievements of the past century. It may even be said that realization of the overwhelming importance of culture came to man as something of a shock. After centuries of speculation about free will and human nature, man's ways of thinking, acting, and feeling were shown to be determined largely by his group and its norms. Each individual, from birth onward, comes under the influence of other persons who are already culturally habituated. Everyone is "humanized," little aware of how much influence the culture has upon him through its representatives. About the only way he can be brought to realize its significance is to encounter severe obstacles in his course, to be confronted with conflicts of norms, or to observe how differently another type of culture could have shaped his experience.

Perhaps the simplest and most useful formulation of the concept of culture is to say that it is an acquired or learned system of shared and transmittable ways of adjusting to life situations.

Some of the brief definitions of culture identify it as "all capabilities and habits which are acquired," "ways of life of this or that people," "patterns of preference in learned behavior for a particular society," "a storehouse of problem solutions to human existence," and "a socially organized, shared, and transmitted body of learned behavior." Like all short, crystallized definitions of general phenomena, however, these leave much to be said, as do similar synoptic formulations concerning biology, health, or disease. A common characteristic recognized in all treatises on culture is *change*, a capacity to shift, accumulate, or lose components, which makes culture far more flexible and variable than are the somatically determined patterns of behavior.

For the purposes of our analysis it is helpful to consider culture in the abstract in order to gain perspective on the general field and to be able to identify the common denominators in different cultures. In the analysis of actual situations, however, culture is specific, applying to a particular group or combination of groups, and its contents can be fairly accurately described.

Here a more formal and authoritative definition of *a* culture will serve a good purpose. According to Ralph Linton, "A culture is the configuration of learned behavior and results of behavior whose component elements are shared and transmitted by members of a particular society."[1] He goes on to interpret this definition by explaining that the term "configuration" implies that cultures are organized patterned wholes; that "learned behavior" limits the activities that are to be classed as part of any given culture to those whose forms have been modified by the learning process (making it clear that neither instinctive behavior nor the basic needs or tensions that provide the ultimate motivations for behavior in the individual have ever been regarded as parts of culture in spite of their obvious influence upon it). He says further, that "behavior" is to be taken in the broadest sense "to include all the activities of the individual, whether overt or covert, physical or psychological"; that the term "results of behavior" refers to both psychological and material phenomena, such as attitudes, value systems, and knowledge in the first place, and the objects made and used, or "material culture," in the second place; and that the phrase "shared and transmitted" implies common usage by some but not necessarily by all members of the particular society, and inculcation of succeeding members largely through instruction and imitation.

The gist of the matter is that a culture is an acquired and systematized form of behavior in the broad sense; it is held in common by certain members of an organized group or society; it is passed along to others through learning processes, formal and informal; and it may be subject to considerable change in content as well as volume, in accordance with discernible

[1] Linton, Ralph, *Cultural Background of Personality*, 1945, p. 32. Idem, *The Study of Man*, 1936, p. 75.

forces and general principles. Scientific problems in the dynamics of changes in a culture are, however, beyond the range of our present discourse.

The far-reaching significance of culture's influence on man's life can scarcely be exaggerated. The functions of his intelligence, for example, are multiplied a thousandfold by his culture. His language, which opens up vast avenues for the communication, accumulation, and preservation of knowledge is the product of his culture. Indeed, all man's advances in coping with the physical environment and modifying his societal relationships stem mainly from cultural developments. Perhaps most important of all for us here is the fact that man's image of himself, his life goals, and his successes and failures in them, are defined and assessed under the dictates of his culture. It is not too strong to say that culture makes *human* for man what would otherwise be little more than animal; and it also fills with stress for him many situations in life that might have remained neutral. While man through the centuries has created his culture, and continues to modify it, culture in turn molds man and mirrors his life situations, cueing the stresses, teeing off his reaction patterns, and tallying up the score.

In order to illustrate vividly how culture can pattern a person's life in health or in sickness, let us resort to a hypothetical situation. Permit us to assume a family secret about the reader and his background. Let us say that your parents were strongly prejudiced against twin children. When you were born, however, you were one of identical twins. Because of your parents' aversion, your twin brother was sent away with a missionary to a tribe of headhunters in the South Pacific, the Kwoma of New Guinea. The missionary died soon thereafter and your brother was reared by the natives in their own culture. He now resembles you in stature, skin texture, hair structure, eye color, and countless other ways. Indeed, physically, he is more like you than any other person. How much difference are you prepared to find between yourself and him?

Here are a few points of contrast between you and him, as derived from the description of a typical New Guinea Kwoma.[1] While you appear in public decently clothed and "sensibly" minded, he would appear mainly naked and downright foolish about the bird-of-paradise plume in his hair. This plume, you will learn, is the homicidal insignia showing that your brother has already "taken a head," perhaps the head of an old woman or child. While you speak English, he would speak what seems to be gibberish. While you are a prosperous professional or businessman, he is a pig hunter and a potato grower, and proud of it. While you are refined in your appetites, this man considers dog meat a delicacy. You may lock your door to keep out thieves, but your brother casts a magical spell that makes anyone who enters his house break out with boils. You will courageously go anywhere in the dark, but this fellow is afraid of ghosts. For protection he carries a torch and wears a dagger, made of a human thigh, no less. He claims, moreover, that he has actually seen ghosts and can show scars on his body and report diseases to prove that he has suffered harm from them. You are afraid of germs, but your brother scoffs at the idea. Instead, he fears magic, and is frequently precipitated into a state of anxiety over succumbing to sickness from sorcery. For your information, he can correlate many onsets of illness in his own experience with spells cast over him.

There are numerous other differences between you and your twin brother, certain of which are more closely related to what might be called "contrasts in personality." But, in general, things that satisfy this young man would leave you sadly unsatisfied, and perhaps a little ill. If you should meet him or try to live with him, you might be disappointed and most unhappy. But any attempt to make him over to a closer resemblance to yourself would probably be fruitless and might have extremely unfortunate results. Perhaps you should not even take him to your family physician when ill. At any rate, he

[1] Whiting, J. W. H., *Becoming a Kwoma*, 1941.

would insist on seeing a medicine man of his own tribe who had already proved his skill in "cures." Although both of you came into the world very much alike, the cultural dies have been cast for you in strong contrast, and the differences will follow and influence you to the very end of your lives.

The real power of culture in the life of an individual lies, in great part, in the use that is made of it by his fellow-group agents. These surrogates, peers, and subordinates select this or that norm or precept and exercise the existing sanctions, such as approbations and punishments, promises and threats, to press the individual into compliance with and fulfillment of the stations and roles in the social structure that are ascribed to him by the culture. Herein lie many opportunities for disproportionate pressures, misapplied sanctions, and the development of maladaptive response patterns on the part of the individual that may intensify life stress and bodily reactions. It is this active manipulation of the culture by the agents of society in key positions with respect to the individual that is so often reflected in the lives and in the complaints of individuals under stress.

Unfortunately, there is no strictly objective and finely calibrated scale for measuring the pressures of fellow-group agents or for the assessment of the enforcement power of any particular cultural norms or prescribed codes of behavior, thought, or feeling on individuals in specified situations. Indeed, the compelling force of a culture mandate, mediated either by the individual himself or by his fellow-group agents, may vary greatly with different individuals or in the case of the same individual at different times. Above all, a person's immediate or intimate associates in an organized group, such as family or clique, may greatly lessen, intensify, or slant the force of a cultural code.

There are, however, general and grossly definable categories of instrumentalities for cultural enforcements that can be delineated for typical life situations and for specified societies or subgroups. Each category of norms has its typical sanctioning agents, although in the last analysis the rating and ranking of these are the products of what we now call public opinion, and they vary with many factors, including the assumed degree of emergency at any time. The categories of cultural norms we shall treat here include customs, laws, and religious or moral precepts.

In general, the customs are the most common forms of cultural controls. They are technically divided into "folkways" and "mores."[1] In the case of folkways, enforcement is less well defined and the degree of compliance is left largely to personal discretion and social innuendoes. Thus, for instance, in our culture, a custom dictates that man wear a tie and coat in most business, social, and professional situations. However, he is not considered immoral if he does not conform to this custom, but merely ill-bred or rude. If an individual fails to act in the approved manner, or to follow the folkways, the punishment is generally indirect but personal, expressed by indications of surprise, disappointment, raised eyebrows, slights, slurs, or perhaps takes the form of ostracizing the offender to some extent.

The folkways are the right ways of doing things in what are regarded as the less vital areas of human conduct. However, they often become involved in critical issues because of their important influences on social relationships. They are enforced primarily by social sanctions of a light, conventional order. The self-appointed Emily Posts can be relied upon to police these customs in sickness as in health, in the hospital as well as on the street and in the drawing room. One should not underrate the significance of the folkways; they can make or break a person's opportunities for suitable adaptations and achievements in active life, and for peace of mind and perhaps an earlier recovery from illness. Only fools, and perhaps prophets, make a practice of flaunting the folkways, and they have rather rough going.

[1] Sumner, W. G., *Folksways*, 1906; Malinowski, Bronislaw, *Crime and Custom in Savage Society*, 1926.

The more stringent customs are called "mores" and carry an urgent sense of group interest and responsibility. Their observance is considered so important to the welfare of the group as a whole that violations cannot be safely tolerated. Public opinion defines the mores in a general way and the public takes an active part in their enforcement. When an individual persists in disregarding a strong *mos* (the singular of mores), he may find himself at the mercy of a mob. In a society many of the individual's acts, thoughts, and sentiments are regulated by these mores, and they can be backed up by self-appointed and rough-handed enforcement agents. In contrast to the lawbreakers, to be considered shortly, the violator of strongly defended mores may be slaughtered rather than sued, as in cases of lynching.

Laws are largely custom-inspired, too, but in literate societies they are generally codified, the violations particularized, the penalties specified, and the enforcement agents designated. Moreover, the adjudications are scheduled and standardized. Therefore, it may be less frightening to commit a breach of a legal rule, and land in the arms of the law, than to violate a strong *mos* and face a mob. Although most of the mores of illiterate groups become laws in civilization, some appear to remain too general for such specificity. Usually there is little enforcement power for a law that is not supported by popular backing, as evidenced by the repeal of the Volstead Act in the United States.

The moral precepts and ethical codes of the large majority of cultures over the world are linked with religious beliefs and prescribed and sanctioned by supernatural agents, gods, or lesser spirits.[1] In the eyes of believers, the gods may express their displeasure when these codes are disobeyed by meting out

[1] Flügel, J. C., *Man, Morals, and Society*, 1945; Fromm, Erich, *Escape from Freedom*, 1941; Idem, *Man for Himself*, 1947; Malinowski, Bronislaw, *Myth in Primitive Psychology*, 1932; Idem, *The Foundations of Faith and Morals*, 1936; Redfield, Robert, *The Primitive World and Its Transformations*, 1953; Westermarck, E. A., *The Origin and Development of the Moral Ideas*, 1926.

misfortune to the offender immediately, or by delaying punishment for some dreaded moment. When punishment is not immediately experienced, guilt and fear over wayward thoughts, acts, or sentiments may be particularly harassing to the individual concerned. Because the penalty is not specific, as it is in the case of man's codified laws, and the enforcement agents are unpredictable, leeway is given for a free play of anxiety and guilt, which may find expression in, or become related to, illness or other physical disabilities. It is thus very probable that much more anxiety is suffered in our hospitals than in our penal institutions.

Very often the self becomes the strictest policing agent of these moral mandates. The cultural codes become deeply *internalized* under the conscience, or what has been called the superego. Then with the self as judge, lashing the whip to impose a rigid, high standard of achievement and conformity, the individual can become his own hardest taskmaster and severest critic. By such standards, which allow little margin for spontaneity in self-expression or for occasional lapses from the dictated perfection, these personalized codes can result in dire self-harm. Under such conditions it could be said that the culture has miscarried, for it enslaves and victimizes the person whom it was created to help.

Thus, the essentials of culture, as differentiated from society, are to be found in group-sanctioned norms and rules, and are recognizable as ideas, attitudes, and actions. However, not all the norms and rules are of equal weight in their bearing upon the individual. Some can be borne lightly, or all but ignored, while others are of the utmost import. We have shown that for a given organized group the cultural prescriptions are fitted together (configurated) into integrated (synchronized) wholes, with each regulated "way" sanctioned (approved or condemned) to a degree that corresponds approximately to its place in the total system. Inappropriate individual responses or group sanctions can upset the poise of the person or the equilibrium of the system.

In summary, these cultural regulations fall roughly into at least three more or less identifiable categories: customs, laws, and moral or religious mandates. The enforcement agents for them are generally the membership of the organized group, real or idealized, and even projected into figures of departed ancestors, gods, and other supernatural powers. We have also recognized that any of these precepts, though perhaps more importantly the ethico-religious, may be internalized by the individual participant, with the harshest enforcements coming from the self.

This portrayal of the cultural milieu that surrounds the individual helps to show more clearly the relationship of the culture to his way of life and serves as a guide to the orderly arrangement of the cultural-personal data in a case history. Indeed, some such system seems indispensable for any systematic assessment of the pressure of a person's culture upon him in a given situation. The culture as he experiences and reports it may be plotted with respect to any phase in his life, but in clinical settings the more pertinent situations are assumed to be those that are characteristically stressful.

Thus, we see culture and society as linked and overlapping in their joint impacts upon the individual. After Linton has delineated, in some 15 chapters of his *Study of Man*, "distinctive aspects" of culture and of society, he emphasizes this idea of the mutual dependence and reciprocal relationships between the two.

> . . . Culture and society are mutually dependent. Neither can exist as a functioning unit without the other. It is the possession of a common culture which gives a society its *esprit de corps* and makes it possible for its members to live and work together with a minimum of confusion and mutual interference. At the same time, the society gives culture overt expression in its behavior, and hands it on from generation to generation. However, societies are so constituted that they can only express culture through the medium of their component individuals and can only perpetuate it by the training of these individuals.[1]

[1] Linton, Ralph, *The Study of Man*. Appleton-Century-Crofts, New York, 1936, p. 271.

Perhaps at this point it will be helpful to link in a graphic way the essential components of culture and society as they shape themselves around the individual during the course of his life. The chief sources of the dynamics directing and limiting the adaptations that a person makes to his life situations

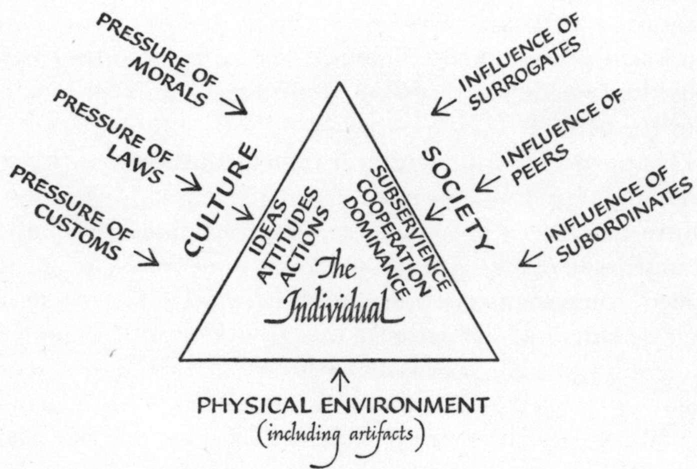

ENVIRONMENTAL RESTRAINTS UPON THE INDIVIDUAL

are fourfold: (a) the biological capacities and potentialities with which he is endowed at birth and which develop within a favorable environment; (b) the actual limiting and restrictive elements in the physical environment—including man-made artifacts—within which the individual lives[1]; (c) the culture; and (d) the society.[2] We attempt to relate the linked areas of limitations and influences on the individual in a given situation in the accompanying diagram.

[1] The material elements of the culture, artifacts, are purposely left out of this section. They can be included in that representing the physical surroundings since they are subsumed in a way under "ideas, attitudes, and actions" which may be related to artifacts and may serve our purpose better when viewed as part of the physical environment.

[2] A fifth dynamic source is not infrequently delineated as experiential or conditioning, which results from the operation of the aforementioned.

This portrays the fact that the individual is not a free agent even within the limits of his biological capacities and his physical environment. He must meet, cope with, and adapt to life situations as a member of his society and a personal product of his culture and within the limits, constraints, and coercions set by the sociocultural system. These patterns are, moreover, subject to study and are measurably predictable, granting a knowledge of the background and of the constellation of factors and forces in operation.

The individual may thus be regarded as bringing to any given life situation whatever biological capacities he may have inherited and had the opportunity to develop. The expression of these proclivities at a given time and place will be limited and restricted or supported and facilitated—boxed in and directed so to speak—by the triangle of environmental factors: physical, cultural, and societal.

The Individual in His Sociocultural System

It is recognized, of course, that no person participates in all segments of his sociocultural system or shares fully in all its aspects. His share in the components of the system, his "cultural curriculum," and his social relationships are selected and "specialed" by combinations of circumstances, many of which are beyond his control. The influence of the system upon his life is not limited, however, to those elements of which he makes special use. A person may be aware of and influenced by many factors in his culture to which he never needs to make specific adaptations. Thus, while playing only the male role, a man may be familiar with and influenced by the rights and duties of woman in his society. He may know how he should behave in the presence of the ruler or chief surrogate, and yet never find himself before him. The same holds true for whole categories of elements that apply to specific subdivisions of the society and the culture.

The cultural components, as Linton has pointed out,[1] may be classified, with only occasional difficulties, in three categories, based upon the extent to which the elements under each heading are shared by the whole membership. These categories help to clarify the relation of the individual to the culture and make it possible to assess which parts of the culture are most pertinent to him.

First, there are the elements (cultural norms and social relationships) common to all sane, normal members who have reached adulthood. Linton calls these the "universals," applying and limiting the term to a particular society and its culture. He places in this category such elements as language, accepted patterns in costume and housing, ideal forms of social interaction, and any general values or precepts that are shared by all; or types of behavior to which all members of a society are expected to conform. He would include also the commonly shared associations, values, norms, and implications that may lie for the most part below the level of the conscious, but that are, at the same time, an integral and vital part of the group experience.

Examples of such universals can be drawn from the common problems of illness. Every human society faces the prospects of sickness and each one has developed its own general cultural adaptations for it, which constitute its solutions. There are identifiable concepts about disease and its origins, sets of prescriptions defining what can be done, and usually by whom, along with standard patterns of sentiments, attitudes, and emotional overtones to guide both the patient and his associates. There are also equipments and procedures for expediting recovery, stock remedies for preventive and protective precautions, ritualistic safeguards, rational interpretations, and social compensations for both the sufferer and his involved fellowship.

[1] Linton, Ralph, *The Study of Man*, 1936, pp. 272–275.

All over the world, as far as we know, whenever a member of society shows recognizable symptoms of illness, fails to meet his obligations as in health, takes to his hammock or cot, complains and waits for others to minister unto him, his customary roles in the group are changed, along with some of the rights and duties associated with these roles, and other sets of privileges and performances come into effect. Thus, a generalized set of sick rules begins to function for those most closely involved, the patient himself and the responsible members designated to take over. It is practically impossible for a sick member to escape, even if he should choose to do so, the impact of his culture's "universals," which are designed to deal with the general problems of disease and possible death.[1]

Second, there are the elements of culture that are shared by members of certain socially recognized categories of individuals, particular subdivisions of the larger society, but not shared by the total population. Linton calls these components of the culture the "specialties."[2] Here are classified the mutually interdependent norms and rules for responsibility and action that apply to only the designated segments of the population, although they may contribute to the well-being of the entire group. He places emphasis here upon the manual skills and technical knowledge that apply to particular craft, labor, or professional subgroups; but ideal patterns of relationships within these units, and the values, goals, ethical standards, and general sentiments common to the specialty

[1] Ackerknecht, E. H., "Primitive Medicine and Culture Pattern," 1942; *Idem*, "Psychopathology, Primitive Medicine, and Primitive Culture," 1943; *Idem*, "Natural Diseases and Rational Treatment in Primitive Medicine," 1946; *Idem*, "Primitive Surgery," 1947; Clements, F. E., "Primitive Concepts of Disease," 1932; Devereux, George, "Primitive Psychiatry," 1940–1942; *Idem*, "Psychiatry and Anthropology," 1952; Ellis, E. S., *Ancient Anodynes:* Primitive Aneasthesia and Allied Conditions, 1946; Ferguson, E. A., *The Theory and Practice of Medicine Among Preliterate Peoples*, 1947; Harley, G. W., *Native African Medicine*, 1941; Holmberg, A. R., *Nomads of the Long Bow*, 1950; La Barre, Weston, *The Peyote Cult*, 1938; *Idem*, "Primitive Psychotherapy in Native American Cultures: Peyotism and Confession," 1947; Leighton, A. H., and D. C. Leighton, "Elements of Psychotherapy in Navaho Religion," 1941; Ruesch, Jurgen, "Social Technique, Social Status, and Social Change in Illness," 1948.

[2] Linton, Ralph, *The Study of Man*, 1936, pp. 272–273.

group also operate and reinforce the impact of its culture upon the individual. The cultural specialties of the medical and nursing professions provide an excellent example. When a set of *specialties* is in any way out of harmony with the generalized *universals* in the same society, an individual member who becomes subject to the two sets of forces may fall victim to the conflicts engendered.

Third, according to Linton, there are the cultural "alternatives."[1] One finds in every society that there are some spheres in human experience and behavior where the culture does not dictate a prescribed and absolutely right way of acting, thinking, or feeling. However, it provides the individual with a choice between two or more ways of achieving the same end or reacting to the same situation. These acceptable alternatives are bona-fide elements of the culture that constitute a permissive range or margin of deviation around an established norm. Linton recognizes that cultures of small societies living under primitive conditions usually include and permit only a limited range of such alternatives, while in a sociocultural system like ours the range may be very broad. For example, in primitive groups a woman's role is largely prescribed, while in our own present society there are several acceptable alternatives from which the woman may choose.

Beyond these legitimate limits, Linton sets up a fourth category which he calls "individual peculiarities."[2] He includes here the nonprescribed but tolerated personal reaction patterns, such as unusual fears, compulsions, individualized habits, and other atypical and perhaps culturally inappropriate responses. Many of these are the results of the accidents of an individual's life experience; they insert the "personal equation" into the individual-society formulation, and help to explain why the ideal patterns of acting, thinking, feeling, and relating to others are only imperfectly adhered to.

[1] *Ibid.*, p. 273.
[2] *Ibid.*, p. 274.

Individual peculiarities cannot be classed as a part of culture in the sense in which the term is ordinarily used. However, the sum total of such individual differences within any society is enormous, and can hardly be disregarded. Moreover, these variations are of extreme importance in cultural dynamics since they are the starting point of everything that later becomes incorporated into the system. Thus, for example, an individual's peculiarly slanted reactions may lead him to found a new religious cult, which becomes adopted by the society and accepted into the culture. In such manner, "individual peculiarities occupy somewhat the same position with regard to culture that individual mutations occupy with regard to a biological species."[1] Further they are of importance in study of the individual, for they may profoundly affect a person's adaptations to his life situations, with some of them harmless and some handicapping to the organism. Here we set in the cultural framework material that is studied from another angle by the psychologist and psychiatrist.[2] The degree of sociocultural toleration for this kind of behavior is, of course, critical to its stress-arousing potentials.

At this point it might be well to state briefly some of the typical patterns that individuals follow in relating themselves to society and its culture. The individual, we have found, may respond to social situations in one, or different combinations, of four rather distinct ways. That is, he may play out his part primarily as a *creature*, a *carrier*, a *creator*, or a *manipulator* of the existing culture of the group, its concepts, codes, and procedures.[3]

As a creature of a society and its culture, a person may act more or less passively, offering little or no resistance to the complex forces within the system which attempt to shape him

[1] *Ibid.*, p. 274.

[2] Colwell, A. H., "Social and Environmental Factors in Medicine," 1946; Weinberg, S. K., *Society and Personality Disorders*, 1952.

[3] Simmons, L. W., editor, *Sun Chief*, 1942, pp. 385–397.

to its purposes. He can be observed submitting to the mandates and surrogates of the system without manifest question or protest, and attempting to meet the expectations of his peers, or even his subordinates, "like a good boy." He tries hard to think, feel, and perform appropriately in each situation. He relies on compliance with these mandates for support and protection, frequently gauging his goals and appraising himself by this test; or he may justify his failures by the same means. He makes a point of identifying himself with the system, of fitting himself into its plan, and of trying to accept his fate.

Perhaps, in theory, a creature-committed person who could completely adapt to and identify with his sociocultural system and remain free of cross currents and conflicts within it, would be able to safeguard himself against extremes of mental and emotional stress, especially those that are socially derived. He could also better tolerate physical strains or ride them out with a certain over-all calm, psychologically grounded in and identified with the social and cultural interpretations and reinforcements. This relationship has significant bearings upon the effects of stressful situations in life experience, whether in the hospital or elsewhere.

In contrast to the creature relationship, and representing perhaps more closely the adult phase of optimum responsibility in the life cycle, is that in which the individual attempts to function as a carrier of his culture. In this capacity he plays a more positive and active part. An individual relating himself characteristically in this way to the social system sets out to exemplify its values and virtues and to demonstrate the efficacy of the socially certified ways and means. He strives to live up to them as a lesson to others, and more firmly to inculcate them into his associates, especially his peers and subordinates, at the same time winning approbation or even homage from his surrogates. In small societal subgroups which he may join he will attempt to adopt quickly the exemplary norms and codes, if not too greatly out of line with familiar standards, and represent himself as a model of them, such as good sense, propriety, and fortitude if these are what the culture rates highly. He may seem to strive under the conviction that he cannot afford at any cost to compromise himself in the presence of his contemporaries or perhaps in his own eyes.

In another relationship, perhaps more typical of adulthood, the individual may be regarded as a creator of new cultural elements that may be fitted into the larger patterns within the institution or society. Potentially, each person is a creator in the sense that he is never quite able to fulfill the prescribed patterns of behavior and may occasionally initiate a useful variation. Whether the variation is the result of accident, invention, or borrowing, it may be adopted by others and become established in the social system. Some individuals exercise this function more than others and seem bent to strive for variations from the customary or routine procedures even when no particular advantage is apparent. During periods of rapid social change there may be advantages to the individual for so doing. There is always a possible gain for others, too, since every cultural advance has it origin in the innovator.

A further significant relationship of the individual to his culture is that of manipulator, a form of response that has not been so well documented in social science literature as the first three. By good luck, tact, skill, and ingenuity a person may be able to utilize the norms and rules of his culture to his own advantage or for any other purpose upon which he is bent. He may marshal them to strengthen his position or to coerce associates into fulfillment of his requirements; or by them he may even inspire other persons to make sacrifices in his behalf. If he finds himself in situations of compromise, he may flaunt certain of the folkways, ignore mores, circumvent laws, or even morals, finding reinforcements in "higher principles," rules of exception, and special prerogatives. When motivated by a strong interest for which he may find justification in other parts of the culture, and fortunately aligned with prerogatives that have given him an advantage, he may elbow competitors to one side and win coveted prizes in terms of authority, position, and special favors.

Our special concern here has been to gain some comprehension of the impact of culture on an individual and his way of life, and later on to relate this to his experience with illness.

In summary, we have seen that in the course of man's biological evolution he purchased considerable freedom from the bondage of inborn patterns of behavior at the price of greater dependence upon organized group life (society), and he also acquired new and much more variable sets of response patterns (culture). This has resulted for him in multiple and magnified potentialities for both adaptive *and* maladaptive behavior. It also has meant that his offspring are more pliable and at the same time more dependent than any other of the high forms of life, and with much longer periods of sustained helplessness in youth, sickness, and old age. Thus is man, preeminently, a socialized and acculturated creature, with a destiny bound up largely within these dimensions of his life. Although free-born, he is culture-bound. Most of the goals, guides, and supports for his existence are both dictated by his culture and sanctioned by his society. Without measurable compliance on his part, it is just about impossible for him to fulfill his proclivities or even to survive. Such is the grip of the sociocultural system on the life of man. This, indeed, creates a major difference in the experience of illness between man and the "lower" forms of life and between men in separate societies.

In our further discourse we shall recommend special attention to the three trunk-line relationships between the individual and his environment. Through systematic exploitation of them, specificity for us may be sharpened with respect to problems of life stress and disease. There are, of course, countless variations and combinations of these forces that shift in impact and emphasis from person to person and for time and place. A particular constellation of these factors may be borne easily by an individual in one set of circumstances and prove his undoing in another.

Then when such a person goes for medical help and strips physically, socially, and culturally before his physician or the attending staff, he may reveal tissue evidence to the watchful eye and vocal testimony to the sensitive ear of background elements in his life from all three dimensions, which working together have produced or complicated his illness. In such a predicament, a clarifying diagnosis and optimum therapy would seem to call for consideration of the combined contributive and precipitative factors.[1]

[1] Bortz, E. L., "Social Components in Medicine," 1940; Cannon, I. M., *On the Social Frontier of Medicine*, 1952; *Idem*, "Some Clinical Aspects of Social Medicine," 1946; Freed, L. F., "Philosophy of Sociological Medicine," 1948; Fromm, Erich, "Individual and Social Origins of Neurosis," 1944; Galdston, Iago, *The Meaning of Social Medicine*, 1954; Halliday, J. L., "Epidemiology and the Psychosomatic Affections," 1946; Mead, Margaret, "The Concept of Culture and the Psychosomatic Approach," 1947; Menninger, K. A., "Changing Concepts of Disease," 1948; Minot, G. R., "Investigation and Teaching in the Field of the Social Component of Medicine," 1937; *Idem*, "Medical Social Aspects in Practice," 1934; Robinson, G. C., "Proper Attention to the Role of Emotion and Social Factors in Illness as a New Step in Public Health," 1945; Roemer, M. I., "Relationship of Social Medicine to the Social Sciences," 1948.

CHAPTER 4

The Sociocultural System as a Stress-Inducing Environmental Factor

THE BROAD OUTLINE of man in his social and cultural setting has been sketched. We perceive in the individual a vulnerable, resourceful, adaptive, and also perishable, human being endowed with certain inborn capacities for development and highly sensitized to learned goals in the adjustment of his life to the total environment. We also see in him a creature of circumstance who undergoes stress and strain from various sources and suffers wear and tear in the course of a relatively short and tenuous life.[1] In his efforts to survive, he is confronted with a triad of essentially different environmental forces—physical, social, and cultural—which serve to maintain him in some respects and to menace him in others.

We know that his culture and his society affect him deeply as a personality and sustain him as a group member. But how do they contribute to his physical maladaptations and to specific bodily disorders? In gross form, involving masses of people, to be sure, such a connection or sequence of experience and effects is widely recognized. Thus, cultural precepts may mislead groups of people with respect to maintaining adequate diets, protecting themselves against infection, seeking prompt and proper medical care, or taking precautions against accidents, overexposure, excessive exertion, and the like. Mass sociological effects on health and nutrition are also easily

[1] Selye, Hans, "The General Adaptation Syndrome and the Diseases of Adaptation," 1946; Idem, *The Physiology and Pathology of Exposure to Stress*, 1950; Wolff, H. G., *Stress and Disease*, 1953.

recognized when pronounced disruption of society's mechanisms occurs through strikes, riots, panics, or breakdowns in the organized systems for the production and distribution of goods and services. No one seriously doubts the import of these forthright and over-all factors upon the health, and even the fate, of numerous individuals as organisms. Modern warfare is an outstanding example of such gross effects with its multitudes of lives snuffed out and of bodies injured or permanently maimed.

In the personal experience of the individual, the biological consequences of sociological stresses and strains along with contributing cultural pressures are sometimes almost as obvious. Within a detailed case history, the general linkage between personal stress and physical debility may occasionally be easy to see, especially if the sequence is closely connected and dramatic. When, for instance, the norms and codes of the culture in a particular person's background inspire in him and require of him, by virtue of his position in society, special heroic or dare-devil exploits, and he carries through courageously with the resultant loss of a leg, an arm, or some worse injury, the sociocultural dynamics and connections seem clear enough.

Within a given cultural context and under particular social circumstances, an individual may quite deliberately risk losing his life to save that of another. Or, if presented with drastic alternatives and left alone with a dangerous weapon, he may understandably take his life under a prevailing code of honor; indeed, he may petition for the privilege and his descendants may cherish the heroics. If he duels where dueling is a duty, feuds when the family folkways call for feuding, commits hara-kiri when it is required to compensate for disgrace or defeat; or if he happens to be a person who merely binds his feet and files his teeth when convention dictates the one or the other, then again the related and relevant physiological effects of sociocultural mandates are self-evident.

If, moreover, because of ill-advised social relationships or the insufficiency of food and shelter provided by his society, a person contracts a contagious disease or suffers physical debility, certain reasonably direct correlations can be surmised between the social circumstances and the individual's physical plight. In short, where the sociocultural and biological connections in the dynamics of disease and other physical defects are closely linked and incontestable, the problem of formulation is quite different from the more usual instances of illness where the process is slow and undramatic, and where the critical factors are subtle, hidden, or even disguised.

Thus, in many of the steadily mounting, so-called chronic ailments that plague our lives, sociocultural components are now suspected of being complicating factors, if not actually the leading elements. But to ferret them out specifically and to demonstrate or measure their effects upon the biological processes are very difficult assignments.

As already indicated, we have found useful a three-dimensional view that portrays the individual as an organism coping with his physical surroundings, as an agent member filling a place in his society, and as a person or personality responding within a culture. While adaptations in all three phases are taking place concurrently and with many interconnections, it is illuminating for the purpose of analysis to direct further attention to each area separately in order to identify the possible sources of stress in a given situation. Such a procedure helps to clarify the fact that critical stresses related to illness may arise in any one of the areas *with* or *without* corresponding stresses occurring in the others, or that stresses may accumulate simultaneously from all three sources.

If, first, we view the individual in his physical surroundings, stresses for him may be associated with illness as a consequence of changes within the organism itself that ordinarily would not be attributed to outside factors; as, for example, in the processes of maturation and aging, irregularities in the functioning of the glands, or in the growth of extraneous tissue such as tumors. On the other hand, stress may be more directly derived from the physical environment, perhaps from the cumulative effects of an inadequate food supply, a hostile climate, or prevalent micro-organisms; or it may result from sudden changes, such as radical alterations in climate, drought and famine, the invasion of insects, or the appearance of dangerous germs and viruses. Hazards in this dimension, derived from either the individual organism or the outer physical environment, are those to which modern medicine has devoted the greater part of its attention and upon which its chief progress has depended.

The second or societal dimension is also a primary source of stress for the individual. Here we see him as a member who occupies certain positions in the social system and has specific activities to perform in the groups of which he is a part—family, community, economic organization, and so on—having responsibilities within each that may tax his capabilities. Because it is important for him to live up to the expectations of his fellows and to play his roles acceptably, his efforts are often fraught with tension. If he is unable to fulfill the functions ascribed to him by society or to meet new obligations associated with each change in status, he "fails" in the eyes of his fellows, and perhaps also in his own eyes, and suffers mental and emotional stress that may affect his health. Such socially derived stresses can accumulate slowly over long periods, but they may also accelerate under trying circumstances and reach a climax at a time when success and failure are balanced delicately. Indeed, the normal progression of an individual in the social structure, such as reaching adulthood, taking on a responsible position, getting married or having children, brings extra duties and obligations that expose him to new stresses as well as provide him with added satisfactions. More dramatic and obvious, though perhaps with less serious consequences to the organism, are those cases where a person's established position in society is threatened by committing prohibited acts. He may, for instance, become involved in perjury and be put to trial before his peers and his own conscience, or he may indulge in some other forbidden behavior, overtly or covertly, that affects his social standing or self-esteem and causes him great anxiety together with correlative bodily reactions.

On the other hand, a man may resolutely stand pat and upright, toeing the mark and meeting commitments steadfastly, but find social relationships changing around him, perhaps depriving him of old positions and prerogatives or assigning to him new stations and activities. This alters his standing with others and creates for him new and unexpected stresses. Outstanding examples are to be found in the occupational sphere in the form of discharge or retirement, and reassignment or transferal, over which the individual may have little control. Similarly, shifts in his status and responsibilities arise within the family through the marriage of other members and through births, deaths, or prolonged illnesses.[1]

They occur also in the larger societal setting with changes from peacetime to warfare, the appearance of economic or political reversals, or even with fluctuations in the stock market, tax rates, or the stringency with which the laws of the land are enforced. Any of countless social relationships that ebb and flow around the individual can at times upset his personal equilibrium and intensify stress. In other words, with a relatively constant culture and a stable physical milieu, society can change for an individual member, much like shifting sands around a once firm structure, and with similarly undermining effects upon his stability and security. Society

[1] For contemporary sources on the family, see Baber, R. E., *Marriage and the Family*, 1953; Burgess, E. W., and H. J. Locke, *The Family*, 1953; Burgess, E. W., and Paul Wallin, *Engagement and Marriage*, 1953; Cavan, R. S., *The American Family*, 1953; Community Service Society of New York, *The Family in a Democratic Society*, 1949; Hill, R. L., editor, *The Family*, 1951; Queen, S. A., and J. B. Adams, *The Family in Various Cultures*, 1952; Richardson, H. B., *Patients Have Families*, 1945; Sirjamaki, John, *The American Family in the Twentieth Century*, 1953; Zimmerman, C. C., *Family and Civilization*, 1947.

always has the power to mar, maim, or even eliminate particular members in either sudden and dramatic enforcements of its demands or by slow, subtle, and hidden forces and processes. Indeed, during the so-called "normal" as well as the "abnormal" phases of the culture, society imposes stress upon certain of its members as truly as it eases stress and provides security for others. It is able under the established cultural mandates to single out particular individuals and place them in especially stressful situations. Society constitutes, in short, an independent and powerful variable in the relationships of the individual to his environment, especially in the activities of its surrogates.

Medicine has not neglected consideration of man in his societal relationships. Some of the outstanding advances in psychiatry and public health have resulted from growing concern with man's problems in group associations. Much work remains to be done, however, in recognizing the various forces operating upon man in his capacity as a group agent, relating these factors to stress-potentials in his life and learning how to put such knowledge to therapeutic use.

Turning to the third or personality-cultural dimension of the patient's life, we find further sources of stress rooted in his relationships to his culture. His personal adaptations to the cultural mandates in terms of attitudes, values, goals, emotional states, and other psychological characteristics may not be so harmonious as they appear. Slow, hidden accumulations of stress and conflict may build up and reach bursting points after years of apparent toleration.

Then again, changes on the part of the individual may upset the personal-cultural balance which has steadied life's adjustments for him. A tribesman, for instance, may adopt certain "civilized" cultural traits to which he has been exposed: interest in the wearing of clothes, or the use of alcohol, new attitudes toward marriage or masculine superiority, the conviction that germs cause disease, or other notions or behavioral patterns that are alien to his own culture. Acquiring these contradictory cultural fragments disrupts important personal relationships in his native society, culture, and physical surroundings which in themselves have remained relatively stable. Conflicts are also produced in his own personal values and goals. Such stresses may be evident in the lives of immigrants to a country like America; for when peoples migrate many elements of the new homeland's culture are rapidly adopted while large parts of the original culture survive in the family or small mobile group. Striking examples are found in first-and second-generation immigrants, and members of such groups as Jews, Negroes, and Asiatics, who because of contemporary patterns of prejudice may be barred from full participation in American culture and become, in a sense, "marginal men" trapped between two cultures and subject to the conflicts arising from both.[1]

Furthermore, a person remaining in the same physical surroundings and with his old associates may continue to cling to attitudes, habits, and goals acquired in his youth, while the cultural norms are changing rapidly, with the result that he is not in harmony with the newly evolved patterns within his own society. He may be left as one stranded with his own personal and outmoded cultural values and attachments. The sweeping tides of cultural change frequently produce new areas of stress in personalities and not seldom leave their marks on the organism. The recurrent conflicts between youth and age stem largely from changes that create for members of the older generation disturbing elements in their personal orientation.[2]

Perhaps now, as we move toward a general discussion of the effects of stress upon the human body, the subject may be

[1] Davie, M. R., *Refugees in America*, 1947; Mead, Margaret, "The Implications of Culture Change for Personality Development," 1947; Park, R. E., "Personality and Cultural Conflict," 1931; Stonequist, E. V., *The Marginal Man*, 1937; Thompson, L. M., and Alice Joseph, "White Pressures on Indian Personality and Culture," 1947; Tumin, M. M., "Some Fragments from the Life History of a Marginal Man," 1945; White, W. L., *Lost Boundaries*, 1948.

[2] Pollak, Otto, *Social Adjustment in Old Age*, 1948; Simmons, L. W., *The Role of the Aged in Primitive Society*, 1945.

brought into sharper focus by directing our attention to a particular kind of stress and surveying it briefly in cross-cultural settings, namely, fear or anxiety.

Fear or Anxiety

For our purpose it is not necessary to try to distinguish between fear and anxiety, nor between the so-called subjective and realistic fears. A threat to the person that can be regarded as "imaginary," if deeply apprehended, persistent, and especially if socially reinforced, may be as effective in evoking bodily reactions as are the fears that are incited by objectifiable and realistic dangers. Indeed, fears that are suffered, whatever their origin, usually have somatic accompaniments.

An important general fact to be recognized is that all sociocultural systems inculcate fears as part of the regular group processes. They may, in the interest of the group, emphasize or exaggerate certain fear elements in particular situations, "making mountains out of mole hills." But, what is perhaps more important, they also operate so as to reduce and regulate fears. A considerable part of society's power over individual members is exerted by means of the controls set up through its *induction* and *reduction* of fears. A given culture defines fearful situations, incites and promotes some fears, plays down others, and provides mechanisms and procedures for the regulation and resolution, as well as the instigation, of fears. It is thus within the power of the sociocultural system, both to magnify certain fears and, then, to diminish them through the exercise of faith, rituals, and other prescribed formulas.

It is widely recognized in social science that control of fear, as regulated by both induction and reduction, plays a vital part in the normal processes of individual-environment adaptations, and that in many situations it carries survival value. The induction of fears is, of course, just as important as their reduction. It is obvious that a completely fearless and foolhardy fellow is no better off than one who is very fearful; indeed, he may be worse off and have a shorter life in that he is oblivious to danger and takes great risks. On the other hand, unbridled fear can become a powerful and destructive force in practically all aspects of life, not the least of which is illness. In individual cases it may disrupt normal physical processes and even precipitate death.

No human society has been found without these group-derived regulators of fear that approach some practical equilibrium in the induction and reduction of this strong emotional force and thereby utilize it in the adaptive processes. All sociocultural systems thus saddle individual members with responsibility, spur them to act with defined fear excitants, and then bridle and rein under the more excessive and destructive fear responses. It is axiomatic that an effective societal system usually functions to define and manage certain fears of its membership within maximal and minimal limits of expediency. An individual member probably is never free from prescribed fears; nor are these fears ordinarily permitted to run riot. In well-organized societies with integrated cultures, certain fears are always *induced* and *reduced*, regulated, in short, within appropriate limits. But all societies are not equally successful in this. Whenever disruptions and discrepancies occur in cultural patterns, and conflicts arise between agent members with respect to the interpretation of and response to fear-exciting situations, the fear-inducing components tend to outdo those that are fear-reducing, thus loading excessive fears upon the individual, which may in turn intensify bodily reactions beyond expedient proportions.[1]

[1] Gantt, W. H., *Experimental Basis for Neurotic Behavior*, 1944; Gillin, John, and G. E. Nicholson, "The Security Functions of Cultural Systems," 1951; Hallowell, A. I., "Fear and Anxiety as Cultural and Individual Variables in a Primitive Society," 1938; *Idem*, "Sin, Sex, and Sickness in Saulteaux Belief," 1939; *Idem*, "The Social Function of Anxiety in a Primitive Society," 1941; Leighton, A. H., and D. C. Leighton, "Some Types of Uneasiness and Fear in a Navaho Indian Community," 1942; May, Rollo, *The Meaning of Anxiety*, 1950; Simmons, L. W., "The Relation Between the Decline of Anxiety-Inducing and Anxiety-Resolving Factors in a Deteriorating Culture and Its Relevance to Bodily Disease," 1950; Welch, Livingston, "Human Conditioning and Anxiety," 1953.

Any rapid cultural changes may result in the intensification of fears among a society's membership in that some of the old fears are left without controls, while new ones may be added. A superficial report on a primitive tribe in contact or conflict with "civilization" may indicate impressive progress as measured by change and so-called "improvements." But close study often reveals considerable evidence of sociocultural deterioration, disharmony, loss of patterned configurations, lags in adaptation, parts that are out of joint; and with mounting anxieties on every hand. When individual lives are investigated, persons may be characterized as fearful, confused, insecure, caught more or less in cultural dilemmas involving the old and the new, and with the securities of yesterday the insecurities of today and probably of tomorrow. Even casual observers may note that the older members of the society, still living by and trusting in the tried and tested ways of yesteryear, are nevertheless better poised and less distraught in the basic securities than are the younger, more sophisticated adults. On close inspection it may be observed that these older people are still quite sensitive and responsive to their culturally defined fear-inducing situations, perhaps much more so than the younger; the difference is that they also rely fully and successfully on their old culture and its fear-reducing provisions. In fact, they may appear to be notably fear-induced persons, but they are even more remarkably fear-resolved personalities.

It seems clear, then, that anxiety-induction surpasses anxiety-reduction in periods marked by pronounced cultural changes and societal disharmonies. It can be held, thus, that the prevalence of uncontrolled, rioting, and destructive fears provides a critical index to the degree of ill-appropriate change, disorganization, and maladaptation existing in a total social system or bearing upon a particular group within it. In other words, fears "out of hand" are to be correlated significantly with the presence of sociocultural discontinuities.

This formulation of the societal control of fear by induction-reduction mechanisms does not imply that a well-knit and integrated sociocultural system is free from strong and devastating fears. It emphasizes, instead, that these fears are not beyond control. A society, through the instrumentality of its culture and the operation of its agents, regularly makes use of such fear-control mechanisms both to discipline and safeguard its members. In fact, an integrated and effective social system may utilize such fears to punish or eliminate certain members who qualify as misfits, incompetents, and incorrigibles. Violent, destructive fears, culturally prescribed and socially sanctioned, are sometimes let loose upon such unfortunate victims, who are thus either suppressed or sacrificed "in the interests of society." Figuratively, and scripturally in a sense, these persons may be singled out and cast into the "lions' den" of culturally induced anxieties to be disciplined or perhaps destroyed by their fears. There is striking evidence in various societies that the impact of such socially induced fears may in itself produce physical illnesses or even death.

For a vivid illustration of the powerful effects that socioculturally derived and evoked fears may exert on the physical condition of the individual, and also of the important supplementary role played by society's agents in reinforcing their devastating impact, we may turn to the practice of black magic by bone-pointing among the natives in the Northern Territory of Australia. Here has been observed the process by which the unhappy victim through his belief in the power of magic, and the reinforcing behavior of his associates, can be reduced to a state of violent illness, resulting at times in rapid death. Dr. W. E. Roth, who served for three years as government surgeon among the primitive people of north-central Queensland, writes regarding the natives' reaction to this magical rite: "So rooted sometimes is this belief on the part of the patient that some enemy has 'pointed' the bone at him, that he will actually lie down to die, and succeed in the attempt, even at the expense of refusing food and succor within his reach. I have myself witnessed three or four such cases."[1] And Dr. Herbert Basedow has provided us with a clinical picture of the effects of bone-pointing upon a credulous native from the moment fear begins to take hold of him.

> The man who discovers that he is being boned . . . is indeed a pitiable sight. He stands aghast, with his eyes staring at the treacherous pointer, and with his hands lifted as though to ward off the lethal medium, which he imagines is pouring into his body. His cheeks blanch and his eyes become glassy and the expression on his face becomes horribly distorted. . . . He attempts to shriek but usually the sound chokes in his throat and all that one can see is froth at his mouth. His body begins to tremble and the muscles twitch involuntarily. He sways backwards and falls to the ground, and after a short time appears to be in a swoon; but soon after he writhes as if in mortal agony, and, covering his face with his hands, begins to moan. After awhile he becomes very composed and crawls to his wurley [hut]. From this time on he sickens and frets, refusing to eat and keeping aloof from the daily affairs of the tribe. Unless help is forthcoming in the shape of a counter-charm administered by the hands of the Nangarri, or medicine-man, his death is only a matter of a comparatively short time. If the coming of the medicine-man is opportune, he might be saved.[2]

W. Lloyd Warner, who has made an extensive study of bone-pointing magic in Australia, has given us a vivid account of the role of societal agents in the process. He has noted that two definite movements of the involved group help to reinforce the effects of the magic on the victim. In the first movement, all the people who stand in close kinship relation to him appear to withdraw their support. This means that practically all his fellows change in their attitude toward him and place him in a new category, as one under a curse, alone and excommunicated. He is in a social sense doomed, and is

[1] Reported in Cannon, W. B., "'Voodoo Death,'" *American Anthropologist*, vol. 44, April, 1942, p. 172.

[2] *Ibid.*

treated as a dying man. He may cease to make any effort to live, even refusing food, thus aiding and abetting his own death. Before the end comes, however, the second movement of the community occurs, the group members return to the victim in order to prepare him for death and ritual mourning. The community now, under an organized plan and with a ceremonial leader, proceeds to cut the sufferer off entirely from the ordinary world and, ultimately, to replace him in his proper position in the sacred totemic world of the spirits. It is not unusual for the victim to have reached a state of mind where he can reciprocate in the emotional overtones of the "last rites," and die with what appears to be complete resignation.[1]

That such deaths do occur has been widely authenticated, although the mode of dying is unclear. Cannon has suggested that individuals may die because of a state of sustained fear and shock, coupled with no intake of food and fluid. A more recent instance has been observed and made available by Doctors Stewart Wolf, Robert Bird, and J. J. Smith. This subject exhibited at no time the tachycardia, the cold and clammy skin, and the hypertension characteristic of shock, except perhaps during the terminal moments.

> The patient was observed in the Southwest Pacific, on Goodenough Island, d'Entrecasteaux Group, British New Guinea. He was approximately thirty years old, and in the Australian Regimental Hospital under the care of Sgt. Hill of the Australian military service. The patient was admitted with the complaint that "pouri-pouri" had been made "against" him, indicating that a potion had been mixed and incantations recited by a person of recognized competence and power.
>
> The implications were that the victim had broken a taboo and he was made aware of the fact that he had been subjected to "pouri-pouri." He knew, in short, that he was regarded as dead by his fellow tribesmen. On being ignored, rejected, and excom-

[1] Warner, W. L., *A Black Civilization:* A Social Study of an Australian Tribe, 1937. See also Cannon, W. B., "The Role of Emotion in Disease," 1936; Yawger, N. S., "Emotions as the Cause of Rapid and Sudden Death," 1936.

municated, and after a period of panic, he had become listless, apathetic, and inert. He expressed at no time a desire to live, and acted as though convinced that his end was near. He had taken to his pallet and refused food and water before being brought to the hospital.

The examination on admission revealed an individual who appeared slightly above his estimated age. He exhibited splenomegaly, skin yaws, and slight arterial hypertension. Although he did not appear severely ill, his state varied between one of frank depression and apathy, without terror, and remaining silent and more or less immobile. His pulse rate was 65, his heart was slightly enlarged, and x-rays of his chest were not contributory. His blood pressure subsequently was within normal range or slightly elevated. His past history revealed that he probably had had malaria, dysentery, and yaws.

He showed no interest in the attention of the physicians. A successful attempt was made to get an anti-potion from his tribe and this was brought to his bedside, with assurance that his health would return. For a short time he partook slightly of the mixture presented to him, but then rejected it. The anti-potion remained at his side, untouched.

He became increasingly apathetic, seemed detached and resigned, barely moved, and his bed covers remained undisturbed for hours. His skin and mouth were dry. His urine contained a slight amount of albumin and had a high specific gravity. He was seen to pass no excreta after the first few days.

He received penicillin, arsenicals, and digitalis. No one came to see him and he interested himself in no other patients. On the ninth day after admission he was found dead in bed.

Autopsy revealed cirrhosis of the liver, splenomegaly, and widespread arteriosclerosis. Also, amyloidosis of the spleen, kidneys, pancreas, and liver was revealed on histological examination. No immediate cause of death was discovered. The likelihood is that the death was due to rejection of fluids, brought about by psychological reactions to tribal rejection.[1]

The chief elements of the situation, the culturally defined fears and the societal agents, seem perhaps more clear-cut and dramatic when we choose our illustration from the weird

[1] Personal communication.

and outlandish practices of a remote and primitive people, but they can apply with equal force in our own society, as indicated by Warner.

> If all a man's near kin, his father, mother, brothers and sisters, wife, children, business associates, friends and all other members of the society should suddenly withdraw themselves because of some dramatic circumstance, refusing to take any attitude but one of taboo and looking at the man as one already dead, and then after some little time perform over him a sacred ceremony which is believed with certainty to guide him out of the land of the living into that of the dead, the enormous suggestive power of this two-fold movement of the community, after it has had its attitudes crystallized, can be somewhat understood by ourselves.[1]

Thus is man held captive by the culture of his time and place. Superimposed upon the purely physical processes of his life are the compelling social forces, pushing and pulling him toward illness or health. The influence which his sociocultural system exerts over his mental and emotional states alone may be sufficient to make up the difference for him between sickness and health or even between life and death. There is tremendous leverage in such a system for coping with life's emergencies. But when illy used or out of hand, the power that saves can destroy.

We would further emphasize that individuals vary greatly in their experience of fear and other emotional stresses, that the social and cultural factors loom large as intervening variables, and that the way situations are defined affects the intensity of the fear evoked. Personal perceptions of threats probably are never completely free of sociocultural influences. Comprehension of the emotional stresses in a person's life is contingent, therefore, upon knowledge of the sociocultural system and how it relates to him. His life embodies general assimilation and synthesis of prevailing elements in his en-

[1] Warner, W. L., *A Black Civilization:* A Social Study of an Australian Tribe. Harper and Bros., New York, 1937, p. 242.

vironment, and it may also represent a selection and elaboration of particular societal and cultural elements therein. In a sense, he is a manifestation of the system incarnate, yet in some other respects he is unique. His portrayal of his society and culture, like his portrait, cannot be matched, point by point, by that of any other person.

While such an over-all sketch of the sociocultural system and its bearings upon the life of the individual, as we have outlined above, provides a helpful layout of the forces involved and suggestions for locating and relating certain of the critical elements in the life situations, the portrayal is still too general to serve as a practical guide for the selection of data in the analysis of concrete issues similar to those that arise in the clinics. The difficulty appears to be twofold: the scope of society and that of culture is unbounded and the situation is unspecified and unlimited. Thus, we shall endeavor, more specifically, to limit the frames of reference and the scope of the data needed for a systematic study of the individual in his stressful life situations.

Subgroups and Subcultural Units

In our effort to bring greater specificity and insight to bear upon the analysis of social data relating to the problems of illness, the concepts of subgroups and subcultural units become useful. It is probably pointless to attempt in detail to comprehend the impact of the entire culture or of the manifold relationships of the total society upon the individual's experience of illness. The subject gets out of hand, and the problems become truly nebulous. Even in the simplest societies the content of the culture is too rich and, as we have seen, the multiplicity of intermember relationships is too great for any one person to share more than limited segments of the whole. Each individual is exposed chiefly to selective aspects of the culture and relates himself closely to only a limited number of fellow members. Thus, the concept of subgroup-subculture delimits the area and helps to direct attention to the more relevant factors.

Societies (whether insect, animal, or human) are observed to be made up of smaller divisions or parts that function as subunits of the whole. These segments of the larger group are based upon individual differences, such as sex, age, or other physical characteristics or aptitudes, and they usually fulfill different functions. Within the elementary, subhuman, culture-free forms of society, subunits may be built up around the existence of such common needs as shelter, food-gathering, food-processing or storing, reproduction of the species, provisions for offspring, and so on. Also, in such subhuman societies as beehives, ant heaps, wolf packs, or colonies of apes, circumstances of the physical environment or assaults from enemy agents may stimulate certain joint, repetitive, more or less cooperative and system-like patterns of behavior on the part of these subunits.

Among human beings, with their capacity for greater modifiability in behavior and with their possession of a culture, the possibilities and the expediency of such subgroup divisions into varied, organized units are vastly multiplied. Typical examples are families, clubs, fraternities, associations, and the like. In number they are literally without limit, and they range in size from small units involving face-to-face relationships, such as the family, to large numbers with a remote and unfamiliar membership as in nations or states. A single individual can hold different stations and fulfill variable functions in many separate subgroups of this kind. Some types of subgroup alignments are universal in the sense that they are to be found in every known society. Among the chief characteristics of the human subgroups are identifiable membership, a body of common interests, a generally shared residue of cultural traits, or specialties, to use Linton's term, and consequent integrated interaction patterns of ideas, attitudes, and activities.

Recognition of identifiable subgroups with corresponding subcultural elements takes on special importance in our present approach to medical care. It gives us a close-range view of an especially relevant subdivision of the social and cultural forces operating in the life of the individual and provides the useful perspective of *subgroup-subcultural* segments of society that deal in a specialized way with the commonly shared problems of disease and health. The concept thus offers us smaller, more manageable, and integrated units for special study.

For the clinician who would seek knowledge of the stress elements in the patient's life and try to discover how they relate to the physical ailments portrayed in the clinic, the subgroup-subcultural formulation may also have a special use. If he attempts such an assessment of the patient's plight, he should know something, perhaps a great deal, about the social context within which the patient has acquired his illness and as much as possible about the dynamics involved. It is impractical, however, for him to attempt to encompass the entire range of the sociocultural components that impinge upon the patient's life. Such a broadside approach leads to the gathering of data *ad infinitum* and without much plan or purpose for their use. A more feasible course, therefore, is to identify the kinds of stress under which the subject suffers, the protective patterns he has developed to cope with these issues, the typical situations that evoke the stresses and set off the reaction patterns, and, especially, the subgroup settings in which they are experienced.

In our society these structured and stress-laden situational settings often turn out to be the family, clique, club, school, church, job context, and so on. These provide the localized and specified subgroup-subcultural units that call for particular attention and detailed data. It is usually in such limited settings that the relationships between the patient and his stress-instigators, on the one hand, and the particular norms and codes of the culture involved, on the other hand, can be studied concretely and in operation, and also assessed clinically in terms of the interests and health of the patient. When for a given individual these relevant and pertinent social subunits can be identified and pinned down for special and expert study and assessment, an important step toward specificity in dealing with the sociocultural data has been taken.

From routine interviews with the patient, different segments of the total culture may be plotted, wherein the individual identifies himself with a particular set of norms and rules for the "good life." One can also spot the areas where he suffers stress under these various cultural mandates, when and where in his multiple-group life he resents and tries to reject the obligations imposed upon him, or accepts them and drives himself onward, and perhaps "to pieces," in fulfillment of them; the kinds of compromises he tries to work out among conflicting memberships and loyalties; the defense patterns he builds up; and some of the inappropriate adaptations which become associated with his way of life. Often what first appears mysterious becomes relatively simple and clear in a systematic study of his adaptations to these subgroups and subcultures.

Definition of the Situation

Another concept that is useful in the analysis of social data for medical purposes is that of "situation." It, too, adds specificity to the individual-environment formulation, and for this reason is of basic importance. Yet, few terms need more clarification.[1]

In clinical parlance the term is being constantly employed in referring to the patient both inside and outside of the hospi-

[1] Bettelheim, Bruno, "Individual and Mass Behavior in Extreme Situations," 1943; Cottrell, L. S., Jr., "The Analysis of Situational Fields in Social Psychology," 1942; *Idem,* "Some Neglected Problems in Social Psychology," 1950; Frank, F. J., "The Situational Approach—A Reaction to Individualism," 1931; Green, A. W., "The Social Situation in Personality Theory," 1942; Queen, S. A., "Some Problems of the Situational Approach," 1931; Reinhardt, J. M., "Personality Traits and the Situation," 1937.

tal, but with an extremely wide range of social and cultural connotations; thus, the meaning implied often seems vague and devious. Indeed, the term is likely to imply anything from a casual incident to a life-long experience.

Perhaps vagueness in the term is to be expected. Life situations merge, flowing into one another without beginnings and endings or other definable boundaries. For specific interests and systematic study, however, there is need to make them divisible into identifiable segments, limitable with respect to boundaries, and comparable within established frames of reference. This is necessary, if only as a matter of conceptual convenience for the purpose at hand. For systematic reference, therefore, it is legitimate and essential to section off specifiable social situations, even if somewhat arbitrarily, in terms of time-span, place, relevant events, and other matters of apparent pertinence to the questions posed. With a particular purpose in mind, for instance, an individual's birthday at a given age may constitute the time span, his home the place, the accidental death of a relative the leading event, and a consequent change in family status the most critical factor in the situation. For a different purpose, other elements or some particular part of the same situation might be given special attention.

Social science itself still has far to go in this type of analysis. Study of the isolated, solitary, ill-defined situations, which afford no basis for meaningful comparisons, are relatively useless for gaining verifiable insights or controls. Productive approaches to such material can only be provided through specification and standardization of situations and by developing objective criteria for the identification of critical elements in chains of comparable situations along an individual's life course.

Perhaps the most illuminating tracer-thread is the element of continuity in the reaction patterns of a person to identical or similar stimuli in comparable situations. This is especially true when the responses are clearly inappropriate, countersanctioned, and, on the surface at least, penalizing. For when reaction patterns are appropriate, regularities and continuities are easy to plot and to predict simply from a knowledge of the roles of the participating parties and of the cultural requirements or norms of expectation and acceptance in specific subgroup units. With normally flexible individuals, behavior is "culture-deep" and fluctuates with the cultural mandates. Personal interests and needs find culturally acceptable outlets, so that the individual's reaction patterns are comfortably consistent with those established as the norms or types for the contemporary society. Such people live up to the expectations of their group and are reinforced in their behavior by the available rewards.

It is the apparently inappropriate behavior patterns that afford special insight into the social and cultural dynamics involved in illness and a patient's experience with it. For such response patterns are much more deeply ingrained and survive obviously at a price in stress and suffering, thus providing a clue for their investigation. Critical elements to watch for are the recurring stimuli, societal or cultural, which repeatedly set off these ill-adaptive reaction patterns. When numerous comparable situations embodying these elements are plotted along the life course, it is often possible to trace with considerable validity the development, and sometimes the origin, of the personal reaction patterns that appear to be related to the illness.

In attempts to conceptualize the personal-situational data, however, it is important to remember that the individual does not possess an entirely objective view of his sociocultural system. He has a personal version, slanted by his own unique experiences in life. This interpretation is, of course, crucial to the person's existing attitudes, his experience of stress, and his reaction patterns. Doubtless, his is the most significant version of the subgroup and subcultural pattern to know in order to perceive what is taking place under the stress. But it is also important to have some more objective and verifiable account of the culture as others are sharing it; otherwise it is difficult to distinguish between fact and fantasy, or general and unique experience, in the actual relationship of the patient to his situation. While it may not be any easier, it is quite a different matter to deal with a situation in which the cultural pressures are realistic and commonly shared, or unique and perhaps overdrawn in the perceptions of a particular patient.

Thus, there may be individuals who become so strongly identified with particular culturally derived standards of behavior that they strive without self-mercy to conform, and who find themselves unable to tolerate their own shortcomings as measured by these self-defined norms. It is plausible that such elaborate behavior patterns, resulting from intense self-identifications, can be a contributing factor, or add complications, to one's physical ailments. The affliction, then, may be interpreted by the sufferer as retribution for his failure, even in a small way, to live up to the requirements of his own personally defined situation. This self-derogatory formulation of his predicament can further provoke feelings of guilt and stress, multiply his conflicts, and sustain an insidious and spiral-like effect upon his illness.

Reaction patterns of this kind carry deep personal and what appear to be compulsive continuities, relating themselves to the "loaded" stimuli that set them off, on the one hand, and to the physical complaints on the other. They also provide a lead for the selection and delimitation of the comparable situations, usually within subgroup-subcultural frames of reference, making possible much further and systematic study of their characteristics, development, and possible modification. The potential pay-off in what we shall call "situational analysis" in delimited sociocultural settings lies in the discriminative selection of key situations and critical elements that seem to be responsible for the physically ill-fated compulsive reaction patterns in the patient's life. Following the design of the socioculturally linked diagram of factors and forces surrounding the individual, it is possible, systematically, to select, or perhaps even to stage, numbers of comparable situations and to plot the recurring reactions and the lines of continuity in situation after situation.[1]

The most important common denominators in the varied but linked and comparable sociocultural situations to be analyzed, as we perceive them, can be summed up briefly as: (1) presence of the repetitive and inappropriate behavior patterns under study; (2) the recognizable recurrent stimuli (social agents or cultural norms and codes in the main) that set off the reaction patterns; (3) limited but adequate scope in the sociocultural frames of references for illuminating contexts; and (4) last, but not least, the "definition of the situation," as this is found in general cultural prescriptions, in the attitudes of key agent members, and in the participant's own personal formulation, that is, the meaning of the situation as he experiences it.[2]

This concept of the "definition of the situation," is basic to the study of the individual in his sociocultural system. It provides a conceptual tool, of some specificity, for gaining a clear perception of how personal, social, and cultural factors are interrelated and continuous in human life, whether in health or illness.

When a person undergoes a new, arresting, or disconcerting experience, he may cast about for an explanation and assessment of it. The shortest and most usual course is to turn, just as a child turns to his parents or a religious person to his priest, to an authoritative surrogate who is ready with defini-

[1] Carr, L. J., "Situational Sociology," 1945; Simmons, L. W., editor, *Sun Chief*, 1942, pp. 385–415.

[2] Hallowell, A. I., "Cultural Factors in the Structuralization of Perception," 1951; Kay, L. W., "Social Norms as Determinants in the Interpretation of Personal Experiences," 1944; Roethlisberger, F. J., and W. J. Dickson, *Management and the Worker*, 1939. Here in the "Hawthorne Experiment" is shown the very significant effect on output of the definition of the situation to the workers.

tion and elucidation. What the person generally gets if he does this is the pat, culturally derived and accredited interpretation to guide his thoughts, feelings, and reactions. In a relatively stable and homogeneous society and culture, which changes only gradually, these stereotyped labels and prescriptions for typical situations, including sickness and dying, will come readymade, intact, and fitted into the larger configurations of cultural norms, codes, and sanctions. These socially patented definitions of life situations become the standard *cues* to adaptive responses and also, as we have seen, the *clues* to a systematic study of the behavior within broad social context.

There is the widest possible range in defining a situation. The tiniest incident can be cued by the culture as ominous and of tremendous import, while something that another culture might define as a direful situation may be ignored as inconsequential. Subcultures and subgroups, and especially the key surrogates in these smaller, closely knit units, have an excellent opportunity to deviate from the general cultural label and to slant or distort the definition much beyond the current standard, and perhaps even counter to it. Or, in a rapidly changing culture, certain of the old labels may become outmoded. Some of these digressions are magnified for particular individuals by the influence of fellow-group agents in positions of special importance, such as parents or group leaders, or by the individuals themselves through their own atypical experience or conditioning in a particular setting.

For an attack of illness, for example, there may be sets of varied and conflicting socially derived definitions. At one extreme, is the alleged impersonal and technical diagnosis, hypothesized or verified medically, based almost completely on physical structures and processes, implying some degree of prognosis, and presented to the patient or to those responsible for his welfare in either a forthright or temporizing formulation. At the other extreme, is a broad cultural interpretation of the situation which attempts to define and portray the affliction in social context, assesses the cause and possible outcome within a complex of qualified subcultural values and codes, and lays out a general course of action for coping with any eventuality. In short, a segment of society provides its more generalized or specialized sick labels and prescriptions, imposes its interpretation upon the participants, and stands ready to step in wherever the situation calls for broader group action.

On the other hand, an individual patient brings to the situation his own peculiar definition, which may vary significantly from the accepted one and tee off inappropriate, atypical reactions and their accompanying penalties. It is only by making use of constant opportunities to check and keep in line with the "official" definition that one is able to maintain harmony with the "standard weights and measurements" for varied experiences. What makes it so difficult, especially for stress-ridden and inflexible personalities, is the fact that the definitions of certain situations may be predominantly subjective and also unconscious, thereby increasing the possibilities of departure from the sanctioned standards. These interpretations of what become the critical elements in life situations are particularly potent and often hidden sources for the magnification of anxiety and stress and for repetitive, inappropriate responses. Thus, knowledge of the origin and development of such deviant definitions and their results in ill-adaptive and danger-laden response patterns may carry particular importance for the medical care of patients whose chronic and inappropriate behavior and bodily reactions bring them to the clinics.

In a general way, the significance of the patient's personal definition of the situation can be illustrated briefly. If encouraged to do so, patients often attempt to sum up tersely their version of the meaning of an illness or to define and interpret their predicament in the hospital. While these epigrammatic expressions, turned over in their minds countless times and repeatedly rephrased until polished, may not cover all the facts, they often provide leading clues for comprehending their behavior during a period of illness.

By prolonged mulling over their plight, some have become picturesque as well as adept in sizing up their own situation and ailments. A college professor pointed up the cues for himself thus: "I am about to break down. I am driving myself to pieces, for I have a Rolls-Royce motor in a Ford chassis." A businessman complained that possibly the leading factor in his illness was the necessity of working "seven and eight days per week." An advertising man stated: "I think when my marital problem is solved, everything else will be solved. I've got a swell boy and a perfect wife; but she is too perfect and too demanding of me. I'd like to come to New York, have a little office, and be a promoter of good ideas. I want to earn $10,000 a year, get a bigger house and a bigger car."

We do not mean to imply that the patient-formulated summary of the experience of an illness, however astute, can be taken at full face value any more than the patient's assessment of his symptoms; but in seeking to comprehend the chain of situations within which an illness is experienced, some knowledge of a patient's own definition of these situations provides useful clues in interpreting his reactions. The point is that what the related situations *mean* to the patient, and how he defines them, illuminate the relationship between himself and his society and his culture, especially his more immediate subgroup-subcultural units.

These definitions of the situation, socioculturally derived or personal, provide focal clues to a comprehension of the individual's previous conditioning and they serve to tee off many of his reaction patterns as a patient. Within the limits of the subgroup-subcultural frame of reference they become significant elements in any comprehensive interpretation of the dynamics of the patient's experience of his illness.

Our attempts thus far to narrow the focus and be more specific in dealing with the sociocultural components in a patient's experience of illness include these steps. Evidence is sought for any exceptional manifestations of stress in the patient's recent experience that may be associated with the physical complaints. The relevant sociocultural subunits are identified in these stressful areas of the patient's life. Series of apparently critical situations within these subgroup units, related to the stressful issues, are delineated for study and comparison in order to note any continuities that may run through them. The prevailing definitions and interpretations of the critical elements are clarified, both those derived from the subgroup context and those arrived at separately by the subject himself out of his own peculiar personal experience. The special meaning of the situations for him is regarded as particularly pertinent and is examined in the light of objective knowledge of the existing social context. These steps appear necessary to us for coming to grips with the more essential elements in the patient's sociocultural environment which may have a bearing upon his adaptations to his illness and the eventual outcome of the disease.

The implications of this perspective for medical science are very provocative. Our study of men in far different societies has provided unmistakable evidence that an individual's bodily condition may be profoundly affected, especially at times regarded as crises, by culture-implanted attitudes, beliefs, and goals and by the actions and interpretations of his trusted associates. Such associates may touch off or accentuate an individual's untoward reactions during stresses or they may assuage and help to allay them through formalized or other channels, with very significant effects upon the sufferer. Knowledge of precisely how this happens, however, must await a far more systematic analysis, and much further research, concerning the linkage between situationally evoked stresses and bodily diseases.

CHAPTER 5

Links Between Stress and Disease

PRECEDING CHAPTERS have endeavored to construct a frame of reference within which the medical and social sciences can collaborate toward a better understanding of illness. The general point of view is that an individual must be seen simultaneously as an organism, a member of society, and a personality in a culture. These three dimensions, with their various potentialities for stress and strain, continuously affect human life, both in health and in illness.

Thus, as an organism man is borne along by his physical environment, but he is also buffeted about by some of its elements. As a member of society he is supported and reinforced by some fellow agents, while he may be frustrated, handicapped, or even vanquished by others. Similarly, as a personality he is both a product of his culture and a potential victim of its compelling or conflicting norms and codes.

Anyone may be carried along comfortably in his milieu for awhile, only to be torn down miserably after a time as these various environmental components of his life converge and impinge upon him. During long stretches of time, harmful and helpful forces may blend and balance, permitting him a workable and safe equilibrium amid many minor fluctuations. What is most important for us to realize, however, is the possibility that the scales may be *tipped* critically at a particular time by a clustering of forces from any one area, or from a combination of the triad of environmental pressures, and that, for the individual, a landslide of ill effects is started.

To assess diagnostically the social and cultural factors that contribute to the upset of this equilibrium at a given time in a person's life is still, for all our present knowledge and clinical and social skills, a very formidable task. Many of the debilitating stresses, often slowly developing and even socially sanctioned, can be more elusive than are some of the chemical elements now isolated in test tubes or the communicable microbes examined under the microscope. Yet, there was a time when these now understood biophysical elements of sickness and death were also difficult to detect. Their workings remained incomprehensible until effective concepts and skills revealed and explained them. Perhaps substantial success in the understanding and control of the presently elusive psychosocial and cultural phenomena in illness awaits similarly effective concepts and skills. In any case, a scientific formulation of the dynamics of disease and therapy that purports to be comprehensive can ill afford to ignore the challenge. If it is granted that physical, social, and cultural factors combine to make man a *whole* person, it is equally imperative to consider their potential and related effects in his *undoing*, whether this takes place through illness, accidents, or other ill-fated happenings.

Indeed, few would doubt in a general way that difficulties in one sphere of man's threefold relationship to his environment are reflected in the other two. The problem is to clarify these interrelationships in such a way as to ease the tasks of research and therapy and to stimulate them. In the following diagram the three factors are placed in relationship to one another so that they may be viewed simultaneously as both *source* and *consequence* of human distress. The nine resulting squares, indicated by letters, stake out certain delimited areas of phenomena, some of which are well known. Supplemented by the following discussion, the diagram is intended to provide a broad outline of potential areas of collaboration between the medical and social sciences.

Reading across the top row of the diagram, it is clear that area A covers those phenomena that manifest close links between physical sources of stress and their physical consequences. Invading germs that produce painful symptoms and conditions typify them. Areas B and C, however, point up the social and cultural consequences of physical distress and illness. It is obvious, for example, that physical misfortunes not only cripple or otherwise handicap the individual as an organism, but also frequently disrupt his life as a group member and as a personality.

	CONSEQUENCES		
SOURCES	PHYSICAL	SOCIAL	CULTURAL
PHYSICAL	A	B	C
SOCIAL	D	E	F
CULTURAL	G	H	I

RELATED AREAS IN HUMAN ADAPTATION

Anyone, for instance, who suffers blindness, loses the use of his legs, or endures a long-term physical ailment is unable to play his accustomed role in society, and he may also undergo a change in personality. In varying degrees his relations to his milieu are disturbed and altered. The patient who had both suffered a loss of his sexual organs through surgery and acquired a permanent colostomy was certainly correct in his claim that he could no longer rely on his former conceptions of himself as a man and that he could not return to his young wife and son at home, to his fellow workers in the shop, or to his cronies in the club in quite the same relationship he had formerly maintained. His experience and treatment for carcinoma, as well as the disease itself, had transformed his adaptations to his environment as an organism and had also altered his associations as a group member and a person. These, indeed, proved to be his undoing in that he lost interest in living and decided to end it all. Thus, frequently it is not difficult to trace and document in detail the connection between what happens to the organism and its effect on the individual as a member of society and as a personality in his cultural milieu.[1]

Returning to the diagram, it is also apparent that areas E, F, H, and I all pertain to the interrelationships of social and cultural forces. From the data gathered by social scientists it is clear that social changes in the form of inventions, for example, have become sources of certain kinds of occupational diseases and hazards, and that recognition of these consequences has modified such aspects of our culture as workmen's compensation laws and has also introduced a specialty of industrial medicine. Similarly, it is easy to see how some identifiable cultural shifts and pressures can also implicate and disturb the established and sustaining social relationships of the individual.[2] Such changes can result, and not infrequently do, in the disruption or breakdown of the organized subgroup units, such as the family, club, church, occupational grouping, and so on. The relatively recent disorganization and disintegration of countless tribes of so-called primitive peoples who have been subjected to "civilization" provides impressive evidence of the effects of cultural changes on existing social

[1] Barker, R. G., and others, *Adjustment to Physical Handicap and Illness*, 1953; Carlson, E. R., *Born That Way*, 1941; Ladieu, Gloria, and others, "Studies in Adjustment to Visible Injuries," 1947; Landis, Carney, and M. M. Bolles, *Personality and Sexuality in the Physically Handicapped Woman*, 1942; Macgregor, F. C., "Some Psycho-social Problems Associated with Facial Deformities," 1951; Macgregor, F. C., and others, *Facial Deformities and Plastic Surgery*, 1953; MacKenzie, C. M., "Facial Deformity and Change in Personality Following Corrective Surgery," 1944.

[2] Ogburn, W. F., *Social Change*, rev. 1950; Barnett, H. G., "Invention and Cultural Change," 1942.

systems and the individuals involved. In our society, for example, the wholesale shifts from rural to urban forms of life, from an agrarian to an industrial economy, from folklore to science, and from traditional therapy to modern medicine have all left significant effects.

The areas of the diagram that are most pertinent to our present interest, however, are D and G, for these include the specific effects of culture and society upon the individual as an organism. We know that his culture and his society influence him deeply as a person and as a member agent, but how do they affect his physical adaptations resulting in identifiable structural changes in his body? How, to be more specific, can it be shown that particular stresses and strains, situationally evoked in a sociocultural milieu, often operating in slow, hidden, humdrum, or even conventionally approved ways in our lives, do actually play determining parts in illness? Our urgent problem is to bring the sociocultural and the biophysical phenomena into alignments that will yield new scientific insights and more effective controls.

The purpose of this chapter, therefore, is to explore in more detail the possible links between situational and biological stress in the experience of illness. In gross forms, as observed above, such connections or sequences are widely recognized[1] but the more subtle processes that relate individualistic and uniquely personal experience to sociocultural and biophysical phenomena are difficult to trace.

In this connection there is a source of considerable error in attempts to correlate predefined stress-laden situations with reported symptoms of disease. Investigators have often sallied forth zealously to collect, code, and classify objectively the existing environmental situations that are assumed to evoke stress. Popularly listed categories include poor housing, marginal income, irregularities in family relations, minority restrictions and inequalities, class and status differentials, low

[1] See Chapter 4.

standards of living in general, and many other more or less measurable forms of situational stress as weighed by specified standards. They have expected to find in individuals falling in such categories close correlations between the "deplorable conditions" and the incidence and type of symptoms. Although in gross numbers their expectations may to some extent be fulfilled, in particular cases no such consistent association can be anticipated. The critical differential more often lies in the way particular individuals perceive, define, and react to a given situation or a series of similar ones.

An energetic and socially minded public health nurse has reported, for instance, that when she called upon a young mother she found the woman in bed, covered with bruises inflicted during the night by her husband. After making an immediate assessment of the situation, the nurse lifted the telephone receiver to summon the police. The wife quickly intervened, however, explaining that she and her husband merely had had a spat, that the crisis was now over, and that their reconciliation had been something to remember and cherish. "Now," said she, "Joe will be exceptionally good to me and the baby for a long time, perhaps a whole year."[1]

Of course, we do not imply that an instance of wife-beating in another context is subject to a similar interpretation. Indeed, the point to be stressed here is that there are no justifiable expectations for finding many close and reliable correlations between objectively specified and classified social situations and neatly identified symptom syndromes. In all probability, as we have continually emphasized in this book, many of the important sociosomatic processes related to human stress and illness can be revealed in their full impact only through detailed and systematic knowledge of the existing social context and the particular person involved.

From this standpoint a more promising method calls for something similar to the life-history technique, but on a selec-

[1] Quoted from a personal communication.

tive basis. From the many patterns of adjustment characterizing an individual, the ones chosen for investigation are those that are manifestly more relevant to a given bodily dysfunction or disease. Such a procedure is based on the realization that it may not be the situational factors *per se* that constitute a serious threat to the individual in a given setting, but the way they are perceived and the amount of conflict they engender. It is not, for instance, the generalized behavior toward parents, power, possessions, sins, sexuality, the hours of work, or the freedoms and restraints involved, but rather the attitude of a particular person to any one of a constellation of these and the threats they arouse for him that provide the key to an understanding of the stresses plaguing his life.[1]

This approach seems even more significant when emotional disturbances are regarded, medically, as background causes of serious organic disorders that result in irreversible tissue changes. In some clinical case histories, indeed, the apparent affinity of the person for his ailment is easily surmised by the physician or even suspected by the discerning patient himself. One patient remarked in a small staff conference: "Yes, Doctor, I know that my trouble is mostly because of what I am, or my lot in life and the way I take it; but please tell me how to behave differently. That's the rub." Such a conclusion may often be easily reached, but the problem of how to unravel and deal effectively with the complex set of factors involved leads the physician directly into the social science area.

In clinical context, research in this area can start whenever an individual recognizes some problem with respect to his health and seeks medical help. Then, whatever incites stress in the patient, arouses manifest emotional tensions, and sets off noticeable protective patterns of response may be regarded by the physician as relevant material with which to begin a study of the relationship of stress to illness in the life of the

[1] Volkart, E. H., editor, *Social Behavior and Personality:* Contributions of W. I. Thomas to Theory and Social Research, 1951.

sufferer. Pertinent data about the patient may be accumulated by observing his behavior and recording his fears, hopes, and fantasies as he brings them to light either spontaneously or as a result of special inquiries on the part of the physician. Events or relationships may be recalled by the patient as having been stressful, or they may be revealed as such, either by his responses to inquiries and suggestions or by his actual behavior in the interview setting. Further, test situations may be set up in which suitable controls are established and mechanical documentation provided while the performance of one or more organs relevant to the symptoms is observed and analyzed. Under such procedures, occasionally, the connection between the general behavior and the specific system functions can be plausibly defined.[1]

Recognition is given to the importance of data derived from dreams and free association, and from analysis of the relationship that develops between the patient and the physician; but special reliance is placed on the assemblage and assessment of the facts drawn from the patient's life history as experienced within the framework of his social and cultural setting. Particular attention is given to demands, values, standards, and actions of the parents, siblings, spouses, job surrogates, and other closely involved persons who influence or frustrate the patient. Through these associated group agents, it is also important to note the preferences and prejudices of the closely knit ingroups with whom the patient has been or wishes to be identified. Further data are accumulated from his statements, his appearance, dress, manner of speaking, gestures, posture; and from his reactions to the company of others, such as physicians, authoritative figures, peer-competitors, and subordinates. Fluctuations in the course of the illness in question

[1] Wolff, H. G., *Stress and Disease*, 1953, pp. 36–43. See also Gottschalk, L. A., H. M. Serota, and L. B. Shapiro, "Psychological Conflict and Neuromuscular Tension: Preliminary Report on a Method as Applied to Rheumatoid Arthritis," 1950; Lindemann, Erich, "Modification in the Course of Ulcerative Colitis in Relationship to Changes in Life Situations and Reaction Patterns," 1950.

are then correlated roughly with events, attitudes, emotional episodes on the one hand and the behavior of the patient on the other.

When pronounced positive correlations with some conflict situations are apparent, short-term experiments are carried out under circumstances in which indicators of organ functions can be set up to measure and record the responses. When suitable control periods of relative relaxation and security are established, the topics of the suspected conflicts and stresses are introduced into the interview, either abruptly or by staged demonstrations. If significant changes occur and are recorded at this time in the measured performance of the organs under study, but not during the discussion of other more neutral topics or during equally neutral test experiences, and if these reactions subside when the subject is successfully reassured and diverted, then it is inferred that the stress or conflict and the change in bodily processes are in some way related.

The chief steps may be summarized as follows: (a) inquiry into the life history of the patient, with special reference to periods of stress associated with particular bodily changes; (b) observation of attitudes, feeling states, and bodily reactions under stressful circumstances over periods of weeks, months, or even years, as recorded in the interview sessions; (c) short-term experiments in which the now recognized stressful subjects are introduced and the reactions of particular organs to such topics recorded through test readings at frequent intervals. Further, the physician may reaffirm the influence of such factors, when through a change of his own attitude to the patient, he is able to diminish or augment the threatening elements in the test situation and observe any change in the patient's responses. In such controlled situations if given topics can be manipulated to precipitate or relieve manifest feelings and bodily functions, it is inferred that these topics set off reaction patterns that influence the bodily changes, though they may not necessarily be the focus of the patient's conflicts. It is assumed, however, that the topics or events evoking the significant reactions are *representative* of the kinds of life situations that are pertinent to the patient's symptoms and bodily changes. By further detailed study it is then sometimes possible to establish which of the features are of more basic dynamic significance to the patient's way of responding.

Needless to say, in such clinical test situations the patient has to act as his own control. This is necessary because the significance of any social stimulus complex is highly personalized, as already observed. Pavlov recognized this problem and has called attention to its importance.[1] Thus, in attempts to set up "controls" and to gather further data, the observer must aim to strike a balance so that his conclusions, which are based on the use of sufficiently long periods of observation and testing, may not be offset by errors stemming from strictly local and unrelated stimuli. He must guard against the effects of frequent repetitions, which may lead to dwindling response potentials, and also avoid prolonged periods of inactivity and suspense, which may result in mounting tensions having little to do with the stresses under study.

In addition to these methodological techniques and cautions, it is also desirable to have some further theoretical orientation with regard to biosocial linkages. Accordingly, we suggest some preliminary formulations and concepts that can be used as a background for the illustrative cases to follow.

Protective Reaction Patterns: Apt and Inept

At the outset it is understood that those bodily processes which underlie, or lead to, physical illness may not be in themselves abnormal or pathological. Usually they are protective devices, "apt" for the task or situation at hand. By the same token they become "inept" when they are invoked too

[1] Pavlov, I. P., *Conditioned Reflexes*, 1927; Idem, *Lectures on Conditioned Reflexes*, 1928.

frequently, or too intensely, or when their action can do little to resolve the particular situation.[1]

We assume that the bodily patterns of response, especially those involving high integrative functions, not only occur as adaptive and protective reactions against adverse forces in the environment but also serve to promote nutritional, reproductive, metabolic, and other normal biological ends. Designed, as it were, for the preservation of the individual and the stock, these integrative patterns fall into two general categories: (1) those evoked by irregularly occurring and unpredictable events; and (2) those that occur more or less regularly, the stimulus and the need being phasic and predictable. The former are noted during crises or periods of transient stress, or unanticipated and threatening alterations in the environment. The latter are related to such normal needs and processes as respiration, feeding, elimination, growth, and reproduction. Both categories of response, when appropriately used under either normal conditions or emergencies, generally function to dissipate threats, avoid dangers, and satisfy needs or achieve goals. Thus, they qualify as apt and adaptive processes.

Either category of responses, however, and especially those mobilized to meet what the individual perceives to be emergencies and which prove inept in the resolution of social and cultural conflicts, may be prolonged indefinitely and with harmful effects. Though they serve to protect and sustain man, their overuse or misuse can make them significantly inappropriate and seriously handicapping. Indeed, over the course of time their ill effects can be cumulative, with the early engendered threats unresolved or the former goals lost, with the tissues damaged, and with the welfare of the person and the survival of the organism further jeopardized. It is possible, in short, for such an accumulation of inept responses to catch a person, flylike in a spider's web, and hasten his undoing.

[1] See Cobb, Stanley, *Emotions and Clinical Medicine*, 1950, pp. 200–204; Wolff, H. G., "Protective Reaction Patterns and Disease," 1947, pp. 944ff.

Cobb has ably summarized the matter: "Our reactions are quite individual but fall into general biological patterns. Just which pattern will be brought out by a given stress is a matter of each individual's past history."[1]

Within this general approach the problem may be defined to advantage, as is now so often done in the medical literature, in terms of a behavioral *process*, including under the term "behavior" not only the overt, observable actions of the individual but also his internal physiological activities.[2] It is postulated that the process may involve inappropriate patterns of response which relate situations of stress experienced by the individual to the bodily ailments which he suffers. The hypothesis implies specifically a linkage between particular situationally evoked stresses and certain physiological reactions that result in disease for the individual.

Of some importance in this connection is that area comprising the so-called functional, as opposed to the organic, disorders. On record are many instances of the patient who complains of, and exhibits, certain identifiable signs of illness, yet the most refined tests reveal no actual organic cause. In such cases the disturbances seem to be due not to structural lesions or invading agents but rather to some malfunctioning of the organ or organs involved. This malfunctioning in turn can often be related to stressful situations wherein the individual's emotional responses overwork the organs to a point of strain and which may lead in time to actual impairment of, or structural changes in, the affected parts. Indeed, it is often difficult to draw the line between diseases that started as "functional" disorders and those of known organic origin, the chief difference being perhaps the point of time in the observation process.

[1] Cobb, Stanley, *Emotions and Clinical Medicine*, 1950, p. 204.

[2] For purpose of clarity we prefer to use the term "behavior" for the observable performances of the individual, and bodily reactions for the internal physiological processes. However, the distinction is more or less arbitrary and will sometimes be disregarded.

In light of these considerations the concept of *protective reaction patterns* has come to constitute a key linkage between psychosocial and biophysical dynamics in illness. It attempts to explain mechanisms by means of which situational threats for the person are seen to have a close, and perhaps critical, bearing on structural changes in the organism. Such a formulation brings into focus the patient as a member of society and a personality as well as an organism; it highlights the situational dynamics as well as the physical; and it explores the *way* in which the individual adapts to the stresses in his life, as an important clue to understanding the symptoms that plague him. For these reasons it is appropriate at this point to discuss in more detail "apt" and "inept" protective reaction patterns from the standpoint of the striving person.

Perhaps the paramount consideration in life is the drive to survive and to function as a physical organism, but for man, success in fulfillment of the goals as a member of society may be of equal importance and his interest in this can become inextricably tied in with his biological survival. As we have seen, threats for him arise realistically as well as symbolically from all three spheres of the environment and are interwoven in the fabric of his highly personalized experience. From all sides come signals that tee off protective reactions in him as an organism. Of critical importance to our formulations is the fact that the individual may *generalize* from biophysical to psychosocial signals or symbols of danger, and react to either one in accordance with an earlier established protective and adaptive pattern of response that is only appropriate in reality to the physical danger to which the original response was made. This is the familiar and experimentally verified principle of *generalized conditioned response*.[1]

It is well known that interference with, or threat to, an individual's interests, or a blocking of the fulfillment of his incentives, causes him to react as he would to assault. He

[1] See Hull, C. L., *Principles of Behavior*, 1943, pp. 262ff., 366ff., 389ff.

responds defensively or offensively, depending on his previous conditioning and his perception of the situation. He struggles to ward off danger, to regain what he has lost or to rid himself of interference with the satisfaction of his drives. In short, he attempts to safeguard his interests as he sees them. Such struggles often evoke emergency protective patterns of reaction, and a considerable part of the human equipment and resources has to do with meeting such crises.

Some of these emergency responses represent widespread mobilization to provide extra fuel and energy to vital parts of the organism. Others appear to be focused on regional defenses of the body, notably at portals of entry and exit. These offensive or defensive, diffuse or localized, protective mechanisms may operate together or separately, but in each case such preparations for action are matched by certain feelings and attitudes which, stemming from the same needs and situations, represent similar strivings.

At such times the organism sacrifices some functions or capacities to the performance of others that seem essential to meeting the adverse situation. But this is a relative matter. Neural processes play a conspicuous role in conditioning these reactions because drives and means of fulfilling them are ultimately integrated through the hypothalamus, archipallium, and neopallium. It should be emphasized that adaptive and protective reactions do not stem primarily from the operation of any one part of the system. Ray and Console,[1] in completely sympathectomized persons, and Scarff,[2] in patients with prefrontal lobotomy, have observed how major neural structures may be disrupted without collapse of adaptation. In short, all organ systems or combinations of systems may participate and combine in defensive, offensive, and adaptive patterns, and

[1] Ray, B. S., and A. D. Console, "Bodily Adjustments in Man During Stress in the Absence of Most Visceral Afferents and Sympathetic Nervous System Regulation," 1950; *Idem*, "Evaluation of Total Sympathectomy," 1949.

[2] Scarff, J. E., "Reaction to Life Stresses Following Unilateral Prefrontal Lobectomy or Lobotomy," 1950.

with integrative and compensatory processes remarkably widespread throughout the organism. Although there is a degree of specialization in the sense that one or another protective arrangement is dominant, discrimination is not exact. In a threatened individual it is common to find a variety of protective reactions, some of which are obviously very pertinent, others less so, and still others minimally effective, or even ill-adaptive, which is especially significant.

Moreover, because man's drives often are primitive, and even violent, they may be out of keeping with his accumulated conception of himself as a "man among men," and therefore unacceptable. Thus, the subsequently evoked reaction patterns may become even less appropriate in his situational setting as he assumes new roles in his progression from infancy to adulthood or into old age. Some of his patterns of response may appear as "regressions" to previous stages in his life and yet persist over many years, thus constituting major liabilities that encumber or endanger his welfare.

In brief, man, feeling threatened, may revert to earlier responses that were once appropriate; he may use for long-term purposes devices seemingly fitted for short-term needs; or he may use as a defense against social or symbolic threats those that are more suitable for the realistic physical dangers. Protective patterns of all kinds are essential and life-saving beyond question when *aptly* used, but may prove costly when *ineptly* used or overused. They are well fitted only for the specific or fleeting emergencies in order that the individual may cope with exceptional dangers that threaten his survival. Although still "adaptive" in a sense, they are actually inappropriate for habitual or persistent patterns of response; and when so exercised they may damage the structures they were "designed" to protect.

This vulnerability of the individual and his aptitude for reacting to a wide range of threatening signals and symbols of danger, which are conditioned by previous experiences and which call forth bodily responses little different from those aptly qualified to meet physical assault, provide a behavioral basis in the organism for much human suffering. Because of the ineptitude of the reactions and their magnitude and duration, the protective patterns may prove to be much more damaging to the organism than the situational threats that evoke them.

A vivid illustration of the fact that a particular part of the body may exhibit patterns of response to symbolic threats that are similar, if not identical, to those called forth earlier by physical threats is an experiment made by Dr. David T. Graham when studying a patient who had presented himself at the clinic for treatment of "hives." The purpose of the experiment was to ascertain whether the skin might react to the threat of a blow, or to a symbolic threat, in much the same way as to the blow itself.[1]

The tone of the minute blood vessels in the skin of the subject's two arms was tested for capacity to hold the contents of the blood within their walls. After preliminary measurements, the left arm was forcibly struck, and immediately there appeared a red area in which the beginning of a wheal could be seen. The capillary tone, which was ascertained at intervals, fell promptly. But the capillary tone in the right arm changed in the same way, although this arm had not been struck. The injured left arm gradually returned to its former state; the right arm recovered a little sooner. Shortly the experiment was repeated, except that now a sham blow was delivered, that is, instead of bringing the ferule down onto the forearm, it was stopped just short of the surface. The capillaries of the left arm behaved just as previously, though no injury was inflicted. This time the right arm did not respond. Gradually the left arm returned to its former state. Soon the whole procedure was repeated, but the subject was *told* that a sham blow was

[1] Wolff, H. G., *Stress and Disease*, 1953, pp. 3–9. See also Graham, D. T., "The Pathogenesis of Hives," 1950; Grant, R. T., R. S. B. Pearson, and W. J. Comeau, "Observations on Urticaria Provoked by Emotion, by Exercise and by Warming the Body," 1936.

about to descend. After this anticipated sham blow, no change in capillary tone occurred.

The nature of the offending stimulus was now shifted. Again the capacity of the capillaries of his skin to hold their contents was ascertained. This time, however, instead of striking the patient's forearm with the ferule, the physician introduced as a topic for discussion a painful family situation, and "just thinking about the things they did to me" made the young man feel as though he were being struck. Simultaneously, the capillaries of the forearm behaved as though he actually had been struck; their tone fell and wheals developed and the skin reaction was clearly that of "hives"; and the role of threat in producing them was understandable. The critical observation, of course, is that the bodily pattern which protected against a blow from the ferule in the first instance could now afford very little if any protection from the socially derived symbolic blows. In short, an initially apt mechanism of response had become inappropriate and now constituted a liability, reaching the proportions of a disease called "hives." Thus, what concerns us here is the identification and analysis of protective reaction patterns involving one or more organs that persist ineptly and that manifest themselves in illness. Then we can attempt to clarify the linkage between life situations evoking stress and the protective patterns that activate the disease.

Many studies in this area have already been undertaken and reports of them are now available. In the following pages, representative materials are presented, grouped according to the parts of the body or functions affected.[1]

The Airways and the Eyes

Conspicuous among defensive protective reactions are those involving the nose and the airways.[2] Nasal dysfunctions

[1] Wolff, H. G., "Experimentally Observed Effects of Stress in Man," 1953.

[2] Holmes, T. H., and others, *The Nose*, 1949; *Idem*, "Life Situations, Emotions and Nasal Disease: Evidence on Summative Effects Exhibited in Patients with 'Hay Fever,'" 1950; Holden, H. M., *Noses*, 1950.

are the basis of one of man's commonest complaints and it has been long suspected that many nasal disorders are related to stressful life experiences. Experiments have shown that the effects upon the nose of introducing a stressful subject in an interview are similar to those resulting from an encounter with an irritating or painful substance. When subjects were purposefully exposed to the "assaults" of fumes of ammonia and the presence of pollen, there was observed in each case sudden pronounced hyperemia and swelling of the nasal structures with hypersecretion and obstruction. There were also tearing, sneezing, coughing, and spasms of the diaphragm and intercostal muscles. The response was similar to "hay fever" and served as a reaction of defense against a noxious gas in the one case, and an irritating "dust" in the other. It was as if the organism were attempting to shut out, neutralize, and wash away the offending substance. These and other subjects exhibited the same reaction of defense to painful stimulation of the head, experimentally induced by a steel head crown, tightened by means of broad tipped screws. In a different series of experiments, a patient whose nasal structures were normal as to color, size, and secretion, was reminded during an interview that she was "caught" in an unhappy marriage. In her angry, frustrated state she burst into tears, and her nasal structures became reddened, swollen, and wet. At other times when the subject expressed rage and desperation and was "on the verge of tears," her nasal mucosa again became hyperemic and swollen, and there was profuse secretion and obstruction.

Such changes in nasal function, precipitated during disturbing interviews on numerous occasions over a period of weeks and months with patients complaining of nasal disorders, were often sufficient to produce obstruction and pain, and they occasionally became associated with asthmatic manifestations. The evidence from the chest in the latter indicated constriction of the bronchi with mucous membrane edema. When such reactions either to people or to pollen were sustained, the hyperemia gradually subsided, leaving the membranes pale, pearly in color, but still swollen, wet, and edematous. With such edematous mucosa and improper drainage, there was strong probability of infection from the ever-present micro-organisms on the mucous membrane. Pyogenic reaction readily ensued and once established, persisted, giving rise to chronic rhinitis, frequent "colds" and "sinusitis."[1]

In a high proportion of these patients it was possible to correlate the onset and recurrence of nasal dysfunction with episodes of stress and conflict. Their attitudes and behavior in meeting threats were predominantly defensive and the shutting out, or washing away, pattern in the nose was part of a general reaction of nonparticipation, an attitude expressed in behavioral utterances. Serious incapacity of the patient may occur when only minor structural changes are present. As observed in earlier studies of headache, many persons overreact to minor disturbances or sensations when their site of origin takes on special meaning.[2] For instance, past conditioning experiences may endow the nose with special significance, so that minor disturbances in nasal function have ominous implications for the individual.

In contrast to the reaction pattern of exclusion during threatening situations was another pattern observed both in a situation inducing overwhelming fear and during times of abject sadness and rejection. Here there was characteristic shrinkage and dryness of the membranes, with pallor and increased lumen of the air passages. Under these circumstances, the organism seems to react in a fashion quite opposite from that of "shutting out and washing away." Transitory changes of similar character occur generally in individuals in response

[1] Wolff, H. G., Stewart Wolf, and others, "Changes in Form and Function of the Mucous Membranes Occurring as Part of Protective Reaction Patterns in Man During Periods of Life Stress and Emotional Conflict," 1948.

[2] Wolff, H. G., *Headache and Other Head Pain*, 1948.

to adverse situational stimuli and usually have little importance. Individuals vary greatly, of course, in their nasal airway reactions.

Since the eyes are involved in the weeping, washing away, neutralizing, and shutting out reactions, it is not surprising to find that disease manifestations in the eyes may also exhibit themselves during such excessive and sustained responses. Thus, engorgement of the corneal vessels and associated attacks of lacrimation, photophobia, nasal obstruction, and discharge occurred in a sullen, rebellious youth suffering from phlyctenular keratitis and in a setting of serious conflict with his mother.[1] Change in attitudes and easement of stress were later associated with remarkable reduction in congestion and improvement of his vision.

In some dejected, resentful women in whom weeping is a feature, a burning erythematous lesion of the skin occurs about the eyes, which is resistant to local therapeutic agents but diminishes when the life situation is perceived in another light or becomes less threatening. In short, the eyes and the airways can be demonstrated to react ineptly at times to socially derived stimuli.

Eating or Preparation for Eating

One of the earliest situations frustrating or threatening the survival of the infant is hunger that is normally experienced in a social setting. In a period of greatest dependence, physical privations are met by getting comfort and nourishment from the hands, and perhaps the breast, of a protective figure. This very apt early pattern of ingestion may reassert itself, ineptly, in certain individuals later on in life when they feel threatened with deprivations of a more generalized and social nature. Then, longing for emotional support and feeling a need to "be babied and cared for," but facing fellow agents who frown

[1] Wolf, Stewart, and P. E. Messier, "Corneal Vascular Changes in Association with Conflict in a Patient with Phlyctenular Keratitis," 1950.

upon such behavior in adults, they resort (and revert) to permissible forms of eating or the physiological preparations for eating, such as hypersalivation.[1] Moreover, the gastric hyperactivity associated with eating processes is manifested by increased blood flow, motility, and acid secretion. In cases where such circumstances have been extended over considerable periods of time, the mucous membrane of the stomach is found to be unusually fragile. Hemorrhage, erosion, and ulceration readily ensue. This hyperdynamic state of the stomach, when sustained, is found to be associated with symptoms, such as heartburn and localized epigastric pain, which may be relieved by food and soda whether or not ulceration is present. Certain neural structures are also involved in reactions that include the vagus nerve and part of the cerebral center. These generally adaptive processes, now ineptly applied and carried to extremes, not infrequently lead to peptic ulcers and other disorders. Perhaps it is pertinent to note here that uncontrollable peptic ulceration in man has been constructively modified by frontal lobotomy, the improvement resulting in part from better relationships between the sufferer and his social environment rather than through specific effects upon the gastric functions.

The importance of sociocultural components in patients suffering from ulcers is frequently apparent in clinical data. Studies on shifts in incidence of ulcerous patients provide another and broader perspective, revealing the following data: In New York Hospital between 1900 and 1939, the male-female ratio of perforated ulcer cases changed from a ratio of 7 to 6 to a ratio of 36 to 3.[2] In western civilizations perforated ulcer cases among young women have diminished considerably

[1] Davey, L. M., and others, "The Effects on Gastric Secretion of Frontal Lobe Stimulation," 1950; Held, I. W., and A. A. Goldbloom, *Peptic Ulcer*, 1946; Mittlemann, Bela, and H. G. Wolff, "Emotions and Gastroduodenal Function," 1942; Szasz, T. S., "Psychosomatic Aspects of Salivary Activity," 1950; Wolf, Stewart, and H. G. Wolff, *Human Gastric Function*, 1947.

[2] Wolff, H. G., *Stress and Disease*, 1953, p. 48.

during the past one hundred and fifty years.[1] Thus, it would appear that, whether or not the incidence has changed in relation to the total population during the past century, the ailment has become more significantly a male disorder and that the severity of the illness, as indicated by perforation, is no longer as common among young women.

This is not the place to explore intensively the possible hypotheses that may account for the data, but such dramatic changes in incidence with respect to men and women support clinical findings in regard to sociocultural variables at work in the lives of ulcerous patients.

If one wishes to speculate, it can be suggested that the "emancipation of woman" that has characterized western nations during the past half-century or more has placed a differential stress in man-woman relationships, with the "pace" of modern life adversely affecting the security of men more than that of women. The fact of significant change in sex ratio for the incidence of perforated peptic ulcers throughout western civilization does fit in roughly with the thesis of augmented social dynamics in disease. Even a brief survey of the corresponding transitions in the status relationships of men and women, especially in the middle socioeconomic classes, is provocative. Noteworthy would seem to be the change in women's attitudes toward men, augmented by profound changes in the social order that have resulted in urbanization, industrialization, and democracy in education, occupation, government, the family, and social life in general. This tide of change can be viewed as undermining the established statuses and emotional supports for man. His position of security and dominance in the family, which was entrenched and reinforced by his culture and society and subscribed to in the nineteenth century by his women folk, es-

[1] Alsted, Gunnar, *Studies on the Changing Incidence of Peptic Ulcer of the Stomach and Duodenum*, 1939; Jennings, Denys, "Perforated Peptic Ulcer: Changes in Age-Incidence and Sex-Distribution in the Last 150 Years," 1940.

pecially by his wife, has been challenged and shaken in the twentieth century.[1]

In the earlier period of male dominance, success and security for a woman were gained mainly through affiliation with men, especially by marriage. The period of maximum striving and competitive effort for marriage as her chief forte was between the ages of seventeen and twenty-seven, after which, if she had not married, resignation might replace striving as she took her place as a subservient figure in some relative's home. Thus, the cultural pattern for female success fostered stress in the years before marriage by strictly limiting her goals and denying overt expression to wider competitive efforts.

In contrast, man was freely conceded the "number one" position in the family circle, and his home was conventionally dubbed "his castle." Within a social matrix of uncontested male dominance he was permitted considerable emotional dependence upon his women folk, and, under cover of his position, he was able to give free expression to, and find support for, his emotional needs. His idiosyncrasies were indulged, his peccadillos tolerated, and his self-assurance reinforced.

With the changes in cultural norms and codes, and with corresponding alterations in interpersonal relationships, the emotional reliance of man on his women folk has become more difficult to indulge and the fulfillment of these needs harder to achieve; his authority and freedom appear limited and his prerogatives curtailed. Environmental changes have swept

[1] For representative sources on stress in family life, see: Bernard, J. S., *American Family Behavior*, 1942; Child, I. L., *Italian or American?* The Second Generation in Conflict, 1943; Eliot, T. D., "The Adjustive Behavior of Bereaved Families," 1930; *Idem*, "The Bereaved Family," 1932; Erikson, E. H., *Childhood and Society*, 1950; Flügel, J. C., *The Psycho-analytic Study of the Family*, 1921; Hill, R. L., *Families Under Stress*, 1949; Lindemann, Erich, "Symptomatology and Management of Acute Grief," 1944; Lumpkin, K. D., *The Family*, 1933; Mowrer, E. R., *Family Disorganization*, 1927; Sears, R. R., "Ordinal Position in the Family as a Psychological Variable," 1950; Simmons, L. W., "A Frame of Reference for Family Research in Problems of Medical Care," 1952; Sirjamaki, John, *The American Family in the Twentieth Century*, 1953; Stagner, Ross, "Studies of Aggressive Social Attitudes: III, Role of Personal and Family Scores," 1944.

away many of women's former obligations to him, and ambivalence on their part toward their remaining responsibilities seems significant in the altered domestic relationships.

While man's position of superiority and prerogative has declined in the domestic setting, his role of responsibility has not been reduced. A wife may become the major financial contributor to the home and gain power to make the key decisions, while unwittingly creating in her husband a conviction of inadequacy. If she attempts and fails in an occupational or vocational venture, she is justified by society in retiring to domestic duties and being provided for by her husband, while there is no such socially approved safety haven for him. And if he should fail to be as good a "provider" as neighbor Jones, he can be nagged and denied the emotional supports of his wife. Indeed, a wife's humiliation over her husband's failure to provide adequately, as measured by contemporary standards, has strong social approval and sanctions. While society's requirements of the male are essentially as stringent as before, the assured emotional supports of family life seem to have dwindled. Can it be that he resorts, and regresses in a sense, to earlier established patterns of eating and drinking or to the bodily reactions associated with the physiological *preparation* for eating and drinking, and may this be one of probably many factors that have tipped the scales in the sex ratio for peptic ulcers?

Patterns of Ejection and Riddance

Infants often vomit and develop diarrhea in reaction to the invasion of noxious agents or with the onset of infection. This may occur even when the gastrointestinal tract is not primarily involved.[1] Hence, during a fretful, uneasy state the feverish infant attempts to protect himself in a general way by ejecting what he has inadvertently admitted. Indeed, a wide variety of assaults or threats may evoke in the infant

[1] Grace, W. J., Stewart Wolf, and H. G. Wolff, *The Human Colon*, 1951.

such an ejection-riddance pattern. Usually before adolescence the child abandons this nonspecific reaction to assault, utilizing it sparingly to rid himself of noxious agents actually present in the gastrointestinal tract. But some individuals persist in the use of the ejection-riddance pattern in a generalized way and even when the assault has no direct relation to the gut.

In studies among adults, it has been shown that an agent such as ipecac which, because of its toxicity, threatens survival, or "amigen" which, because of its unesthetic qualities of texture and taste, is unacceptable or revolting, elicits anorexia and feelings of nausea. The motility and tone of the stomach diminishes, the acid secretion decreases, while mucous secretion and salivation increase and vomiting subsequently occurs. Such an increase in mucous secretion dilutes, neutralizes, and washes away the noxious agent. This, coupled with the motor pattern that empties the stomach through the esophagus and mouth, would be maximally effective in protecting an organism against an ingested poison.

Likewise, unacceptable or offensive situations, or those eliciting feelings of disgust, are often associated with anorexia and sensations of nausea, with increased secretion of mucous, and with depressed digestive functions. With the added mucous secretion in the stomach, salivary secretion also increases. Under these circumstances, subjects complain of anorexia, distention, gastric fullness, belching, retention of food in the stomach, "dyspepsia," and, ultimately, vomiting. In this manner, situations which the individual finds unacceptable either because of their noxious or poisonous pharmacodynamic effect, or because they otherwise constitute an assault or threat to an individual's security, are associated with a protective reaction pattern involving dilution, neutralization, and ejection of the contents of the stomach.

Situations or symbols, because of their significance to the individual, can also cause him to feel equally overwhelmed or evoke in him feelings of disgust, desperation, or revolt that become associated with similar gastric reactions. Sometimes there may occur almost complete cessation of gastric activity. This is compatible with the view that an assault that has shocked and perhaps overwhelmed the organism evokes a pattern in which the digestive function is all but irrelevant and therefore abolished. Studies of gastric hypodynamic reactions indicate that there are two patterns that are closely linked and often coexistent: (1) a pattern associated with overwhelming catastrophe, with feelings of fear, terror, abject grief, depression, and despair, in which practically all gastric function comes to a standstill; (2) a pattern also often associated with these feelings or with threats and assaults that elicit feelings of disgust and contempt and that, because of an early experience of the subject, are associated with the ejection reactions. In this protective reaction pattern of defense, gastric function is also reduced, but mucous production is increased, as is also duodenal motor function, and the concomitant skeletal muscle contractions seen in vomiting result. Again the organism behaves as though the noxious incident inadvertently ingested could be diluted, neutralized, and ejected.

A person who is confronted by overwhelming environmental affronts, assaults, or demands may generalize the pattern of ejection and riddance. One who "takes on more than he can handle," who feels inadequate to the demands of his life situation, or is thwarted and filled with hatred, defiance, contempt, and suppressed or unconscious needs to be rid of a threatening situation, yet passive withal, may have bouts of diarrhea. However, the riddance pattern may be so integrated in the patient's over-all behavior that the subject who exhibits violent diarrhea may also appear calm, sweet, and serene. In fact, it is commonly observed that the patient with ulcerative colitis is characteristically and outwardly a calm and superficially peaceful individual of more than usual dependence.[1] On going beneath this calm exterior it becomes apparent that he is "sitting on a powder keg" of stress, such as anxiety, hostility, resentment, and guilt. These long-standing unrelieved feelings are associated with the hyperfunction exhibited in increased motility, increased vascularity, turgescence, and hemorrhagic lesions of the colon. Increased concentrations of lysozyme are often found.[2] The combination of hypermotility, hypervascularity, hemorrhages, increased fragility of the mucous membranes and great numbers of organisms in the large intestines may lead to the symptoms characteristic of ulcerative colitis.

Skeletal Muscles and Cranial Arteries

Not only are mucous membranes and smooth muscles and glands involved in protective reactions; skeletal muscles are also integrated into such patterns. Familiar examples are the various body postures of alertness or abjectness associated with states of tension and despair.[3] Some of these sustained skeletal muscle patterns give rise to complaints. Muscles may be the source of pain and tenderness after steady voluntary activity of relatively short periods lasting no longer than a few minutes. Tenderness in muscles that have been continuously contracted for hours or days may outlast the actual contraction as it does after unaccustomed exercise. A host of headaches, backaches, aches of extremities, and paresthesia in tense, dissatisfied, resentful people similarly result from continued contraction of skeletal muscles manifesting sustained and inappropriate bodily alertness and readiness to act in response to actual or symbolic threats.

[1] Grace, W. J., and H. G. Wolff, "Treatment of Ulcerative Colitis," 1951; Prugh, D. G., "Variations in Attitudes, Behavior, and Feeling-States as Exhibited in the Play of Children During Modifications in the Course of Ulcerative Colitis," 1950.

[2] Grace, W. J., "Life Situations, Emotions and Chronic Ulcerative Colitis," 1950; Groen, Jacques, "Psychogenesis and Psychotherapy of Ulcerative Colitis," 1947.

[3] Holmes, T. H., and H. G. Wolff, "Life Situations, Emotions and Backache," 1950.

Headache, perhaps the commonest complaint that confronts physicians,[1] is in nine out of ten instances a manifestation of life stress and is coupled with anger and striving. It usually results from the distention of cranial arteries alone or in combination with sustained contraction of skeletal muscles about the head and neck. Sometimes the latter, as just described, is the prime cause of the pain. Studies of representative cranial arteries in persons with vascular headaches have shown that progressive dilation and distention of involved arteries occur following the onset of vascular headache. This alteration in the arterial wall was associated with increasing intensity of pain. As the attack subsided either spontaneously or after the administration of agents and procedures, the distention and pain diminished concurrently, while the artery returned to its former state. In persons suffering from unilateral headache this sequence of vascular changes occurred only on the painful side. In those having bilateral headache, arteries on both sides of the head were involved; when the headache moved from one side to the other during a single attack, there was a corresponding change in the condition of the cranial arteries, first on the one side and then on the other.

Persons suffering from vascular headache of the migraine type quite commonly have the attitude "I must do it better and longer than others" and are noted to have exceedingly "labile" cranial arteries as contrasted with subjects who never have headaches. The latter exhibit little alteration in the state of the cranial arteries in response to excessive work demands, frustrations, or stress-arousing interviews. In contrast, those who experience vascular headaches readily respond to the discussion of threatening topics with dilation and distention of cranial arteries. Cranial vasoconstrictive phenomena precede the actual headache phase of the attack. Characteristic attacks

[1] Wolff, H. G., *Headache and Other Head Pain*, 1948; Tunis, Martin, and others, "Studies on Headache: Further Observations on Cranial and Conjunctival Vessels During and Between Vascular Headache Attacks," 1951.

of vascular headaches are repeatedly precipitated in such persons by the revival of what are to them threatening situations. These excessive responses obviously become inappropriate and handicapping.

Over-all Mobilization and the Heart

Measurements have been made, before and after exercise, of the pulse, blood pressure, ventilatory index (the amount of oxygen utilized in terms of the amount of air breathed in), cardiac output, and stroke volume.[1] It was found, for example, that when a certain healthy individual who felt shy and incompetent when speaking in public was asked to lead a particular discussion, he exhibited in response to the standard exercise test a striking increase in blood pressure and stroke volume, and a decrease in ventilatory efficiency. This augmented response to a standard test for measurements persisted for forty-eight hours after the talk turned out to be, in his judgment, a complete failure. Changes of a similar nature and duration were linked to anger and tension.

During periods of domestic difficulties healthy subjects have exhibited physiological inefficiency in failing to return to the initial resting state after a standard exercise. Similar impairment of the subject's ability to return to the resting state was observed after a night during which the subject had had only three hours' sleep. A healthy person also reacted with similar decreases in circulatory efficiency to the assault of a minor infection, and likewise to a fellow worker's remarks that contained an implication of inadequacy.

In short, the heart of the healthy, relaxed subject responds to the standard exercise situation with increases in stroke volume and output, which within approximately two minutes return to the initial resting level. When the same individual

[1] Wolff, H. G., "Life Stress and Cardiovascular Disorders," 1950; Wolf, G. A., Jr., and H. G. Wolff, "Studies on the Nature of Certain Symptoms Associated with Cardiovascular Disorders," 1946.

is under stress, the performance of his heart while at rest may be unaltered and may respond to exercise in the usual adequate fashion. But quite often after exercise it continues to behave as though he were still doing extra work and only slowly returns to the resting level of performance. It is suggested that under these conditions an already fragile organ is operating ineptly and may by so doing suffer further serious impairment of function.

The Large Bowel: Constipation

Protective reaction patterns designed to mobilize for action and that involve skeletal muscles and pressor cardiovascular responses are often associated with constipation. During such bodily preparation for action, delayed emptying of the bowel may be appropriate.[1] It is well known that the urge to defecate does not occur during violent exercise, competitive sports, and prolonged activities, such as sailing races. Constipation shown to be associated with colonic hypofunction is in part a skeletal muscle phenomenon and not exclusively the result of a faulty bowel function. The external sphincter, made up principally of skeletal muscle and innervated by somatic nerves, may participate in a pattern of widespread skeletal muscle contraction involving especially the neck, back, perineal region, and parts of the extremities.

The evidence concerning the mechanism of constipation may be briefly stated as follows. By administering barium by mouth to patients with constipation it was revealed that the large bowel was slack and elongated. Also, with the exception of the sigmoid, colonic contraction waves were absent or minimal. The sigmoid colon exhibited nonpropulsive rhythmic contractions. The feces deposited and compressed in the rectum were dehydrated and remained there for longer than the

[1] Almy, T. P., and others, "Constipation and Diarrhea as Reactions to Life Stress," 1950; Grace, W. J., Stewart Wolf, and H. G. Wolff, *The Human Colon*, 1951; White, B. V., and others, *Mucous Colitis:* A Psychological Study of Sixty Cases, 1939.

usual period. Such a hypodynamic state of the bowel was associated with feelings of dejection, futility, and discouraged strivings. Spasm of the rectal sphincter alone or as a part of a widespread skeletal muscle tension was often associated with hypermotility of the large bowel.

During a phase of diarrhea, x-ray studies of the same or different individuals showed that the bowel was narrower and shortened and that contraction waves were conspicuous. Such a condition of the bowel was associated with situations ininvolving fear, panic, and the feeling of being suddenly confronted by more than could be managed.

The formulation that most satisfactorily embraces the experimental observations is as follows: An active gastrocolic reflex, usually initiated by eating, induces propulsive contraction waves in the cecum, which ascend and transverse the colon with sustained contractions of longitudinal muscles on the left side, thus shortening the colon so that feces are pushed into the sigmoid and rectum. The then distended rectum, under optimal circumstances, accentuates the colonic propulsive activity (mass reflex) which in turn sets off defecation reflexes, including the relaxation of the sphincters. The arrangement of forces in defecation thus resembles that exhibited when an uncapped tube of toothpaste is pushed from the bottom, the longitudinal projection of energy propelling and ejecting the tube's contents. Situations evoking sadness, dejection, or cheerless striving may inhibit the gastrocolic reflex, induce nonpropulsive phasic contractions in the sigmoid, and interfere with the mass reflex. It has been suggested that during such stress reactions the nonpropulsive contraction of the sigmoid and spasm at the sigmoid-rectal junction actually prevent the expulsion of the contents of the large bowel into the rectum. Regardless of whether such retarding effect is exercised by the sigmoid, there is a failure of propulsion, coupled with contraction of the sphincters and prolonged retention of the feces. It is as though the individual, unable to face and grapple with the threat, was nevertheless, firmly "holding on," or tensely awaiting an attack that is indefinitely delayed. The individual so poised is not in a state optimal for defecation and may be inept in performance.

Basic Alterations in Metabolism

There is increasing evidence,[1] that basic adaptive responses to the danger of starvation may be utilized inappropriately during other threatening periods of longer or shorter duration.

Events either consciously or unconsciously interpreted as threats to security have been shown to produce in both diabetic and nondiabetic persons a rise in the ketone bodies in the venous blood and fluctuations in the blood sugar level. The magnitude of these reactions was greater in diabetic persons, and when large enough and of sufficient duration led to ketosis and hyperglycemia in some, and to hypoglycemia in others, without the intervention of other factors such as intercurrent infections, changes in physical activity, or alteration of insulin and of food intake. During periods of stress a diuresis was produced in both diabetic and nondiabetic persons. In a diabetic such diuresis was associated with a massive loss of glucose and electrolytes, important in the development of dehydration and coma.

Diabetes mellitus has not been widely viewed as an inappropriate use of an adaptive mechanism, primarily because it has not been recognized generally that there could be an earlier life situation to which a metabolic rearrangement of such a nature would represent an apt and adequate response.

There is, however, a situation in which the normal, healthy human develops a "diabetes mellitus," namely, starvation. In

[1] See Hinkle, L. E., Jr., and Stewart Wolf, "Studies in Diabetes Mellitus: Changes in Glucose, Ketone, and Water Metabolism During Stress," 1950; Hinkle, L. E., Jr., C. J. Edwards, and Stewart Wolf, "Studies in Diabetes Mellitus: The Occurrence of a Diuresis in Diabetic Persons Exposed to Stressful Life Situations . . . ," 1951; Rosen, Harold, and Theodore Lidz, "Emotional Factors in the Precipitation of Recurrent Diabetic Acidosis," 1949.

the absence of food for more than approximately twenty-four hours, the human mechanism ceases in part to metabolize carbohydrate and turns to the use of fat as a body fuel. The respiratory quotient falls, and the liver begins to pour ketone bodies into the blood until they reach levels as high as 60 mg. per cent.[1] Furthermore, if carbohydrate is then fed to the subject, the blood sugar promptly rises to hyperglycemic levels, producing a "diabetic glucose tolerance curve," and the glucose is promptly excreted in the urine. The serum potassium and inorganic phosphate levels do not fall, and pyruvic acid does not increase in the blood, as it would if appreciable amounts of glucose were being metabolized by the muscle.[2] Mammals are unable to store glucose in amounts sufficient to sustain the blood sugar level during prolonged periods of starvation and they must rely upon glucose derived mainly from body protein. Since the function of the nervous system is dependent upon a constant supply of glucose and cannot operate effectively in the face of a sustained hypoglycemia,[3] the prolonging of life during starvation demands that glucose be conserved in order to minimize destruction of body protein. Since man can perform effectively on whole fat or ketone bodies, this demand is met primarily by increasing the utilization of fat in both forms, and by restricting the utilization of glucose in muscles. Whether or not fatty acids can be converted to glucose has not been determined, but there is no doubt that a large part of the glucose consumed during starvation is produced from body protein and that the attendant wasting of body tissues must be kept at a minimum if life is to be prolonged. Protein is the only major source of glucose from body tissues. The use of fat instead of glucose is therefore doubly valuable in starvation.

[1] Crandall, L. A., Jr., "A Comparison of Ketosis in Man and Dog," 1941.

[2] Wollenberger, A., and M. A. Linton, Jr., "The Metabolism of Glucose in Starvation and Water Deprivation," 1947.

[3] Baker, Zelma, J. F. Fagekas, and H. E. Himwich, "Carbohydrate Oxidation in Normal and Diabetic Cerebral Tissues," 1938.

Adaptations to the initial phases of starvation is also characterized by a transient diuresis and in partially starved individuals thirst and polyuria may be distressing.[1] In this respect also starvation resembles diabetes.

The diuresis that occurs at the onset of starvation also has been found to occur in a setting of anxiety experienced by many people with and without diabetes. In diabetes it may be produced experimentally in the absence of glycosuria, of which it is independent. When such stress diuresis is induced in a diabetic who has glycosuria, the rate of glucose and chloride excretion is independent of ketonuria and accounts for much of the loss of fixed base and of the dehydration that may occur in diabetic acidosis. The rise in glucose excretion is independent of changes in the level of the blood glucose, which may fall as the rate of excretion rises. These facts have raised the interesting question of whether the polyuria of diabetic persons is a result of glycosuria, or if glycosuria may not be in part a result of polyuria, which in turn is a part of the metabolic adaptation to life stress.

Since a fall of blood sugar was commonly noted in diabetics during experimentally induced threats, it is suggested that in the presence of excessive carbohydrate intake, adjustments made to maintain adequate blood sugar levels in the face of threats lead to overcompensation in the form of hyperglycemia. In short, no qualitative difference between the metabolism of starvation and that of early, mild diabetes has been demonstrated. However, if a starving man is fed carbohydrate, his metabolism soon responds to the cue that food is present; within a few hours his respiratory quotient rises, his "diabetic tolerance curve" and glycosuria disappear, and the secondary metabolic effects of glucose utilization are seen in the blood. The diabetic does not respond to this cue. The ingested glucose therefore accumulates in his blood to hyperglycemic levels, and spills into the urine. The diabetic seems

[1] Keys, A. B., and others, *The Biology of Human Starvation*, 1950.

to continue to use the adaptation to starvation though he is not deprived of food.

An explanation is suggested by Hinkle for the use of the pattern of reaction as if to food deprivation in the midst of plenty.[1] In his patients the onset of diabetic disorder occurred after a period of stress characterized by loss of loved persons, objects, or relationships regarded by them as indispensable. They reacted as if they had been deprived of much needed love and support; this deprivation aroused hostility, often focused upon the parent figure whose love they most desired. Their craving for love and support was therefore complicated by an inability to accept it. Even in their earliest infancy and childhood they reacted to such stresses as the illness of the mother, the birth of a sibling, or rejection by parents with an increase in appetite, increase in weight, and demand for sweets. The parents often remarked on this, saying, "He always ate more than the other children," or "He was always asking for sweets, even from the time he was a little baby."

Since in earliest infancy the relation between food and mother love is very close, security and love became associated with food-getting throughout life, and the starvation pattern may be evoked in response to the absence of either food or love. The diabetic patient reacts as though food and security were identical and develops a physiological reaction appropriate to starvation at a time when he is exposed to deprivations other than those of food. In this same sense, then, diabetes mellitus may be viewed as the inappropriate use of an adaptive reaction. For short periods such a response, though clumsy, might be harmless, but through long-continued use it is associated with the irreversible changes of function and structure characteristically found in diabetics. Life crises in the diabetic may evoke an exacerbation of the pattern of fat and ketone utilization leading to ketosis, coma, and death.

[1] Hinkle, L. E., Jr., and Stewart Wolf, "Studies in Diabetes Mellitus: Changes in Glucose, Ketone, and Water Metabolism During Stress," 1950.

Toward the Linkage of Medicosocial Concepts

Time and space, as well as the general purpose of this study, have permitted only sampled and sketchy accounts of the research that advances our understanding of protective reaction patterns as related to stress and disease. A more thorough survey of the clinical and experimental studies, including current work, would afford further evidence of the significance of situationally evoked stresses for disease-forming processes.[1] There are, however, gaps in the life-history sequence of social phenomena and personal experience that are not easily bridged by existing knowledge in either medicine or the social sciences. In these circumstances we can only suggest those formulations that on the basis of our thought and experience, seem most promising.

A formulation that portrays a sequence such as the following is clearly incomplete and may be misleading: typical situation → specified stress → particular reaction pattern → identifiable structural change. It leaves significant gaps in the chain of sequences. The missing links may be indicated as: typical situation → ? → specified stress → ? → particular reaction pattern → ? → identifiable structural change. The interrogation points represent the possible intervening variables that tie situation to stress, stress to reaction, and reaction to illness. The conclusion emerges that these relatively unknown components play a large part in tipping the scales in the individual-environment balance in ways to aggravate stress, activate reactions, and debilitate some persons and not others. It would appear obvious that these missing links, or puzzling variables, challenge research in the social as well as in the physical sciences.

In our opinion medicosocial collaboration can proceed most fruitfully by recognizing that the third linkage, that between

[1] Cannon, W. B., *The Wisdom of the Body*, 1939; Idem, *Bodily Changes in Pain, Hunger, Fear and Rage*, 1929; Beale, B. B., and others, "A Clinical Guide to Prognosis in Stress Diseases," 1952.

particular reaction pattern and identifiable structural change, can best be studied by medical and physical sciences; that the first linkage—between typical situation and specified stress—is clearly within the province of the social sciences; and that it is the joint province of both social and physical (or medical) scientists to work on the central linkage, namely, how specified stresses evoke particular protective reaction patterns. We now turn to a discussion of those linkages that particularly involve medical-social collaboration.

The central problem of the first linkage, that between situation and stress, may be profitably viewed by recalling that the individual is obliged to adapt himself to all three spheres of his environment, physical, social, and cultural, simultaneously and that these *may be in sharp conflict.* Response patterns that are highly prized in social and cultural context can prove very ill advised and inappropriate in the physical sphere, or vice versa, as we have illustrated in Chapter 4.

In particular instances, individuals may be trapped into illness or debility by the contradictions that exist between the socially imperative and physically inappropriate pattern of behavior. Within such situations where deliberate choices involving overt behavior are apparent, and where actions are followed immediately by dramatic consequences, a response that seems initially as of minor importance can "trip the treadle of the trap" and end in major physical impairment.

When, for example, the nine-year-old boy, Tom, mistakenly took a quick swallow of steaming hot chowder from what appeared to be a cool mug in his mother's kitchen and held the hot broth in his mouth through fear of soiling the spotless floor and of facing her wrath, his behavior becomes understandable in social context. Through conditioning, especially within the family subgroup, he perhaps felt it imperative not to spew the liquid onto the floor. But his throat was scalded to such an extent that it became permanently closed and necessitated a gastrostomy. Tom required tube-feeding for the rest of his life. In this case the connections between the situational conflict and the ill-fated consequence are easy to see.[1]

Yet, no less severe consequences, resulting from psychosocial pressures, may be wrought upon the organism in "slow motion" and more subtly over extended periods of time. Years later Doctor Stewart Wolf was able to demonstrate in the same Tom, then an independent and determined man, that states of fear and anxiety experienced by him, and prompted by what he considered to be unfair accusations and personal affronts, could cause him to discharge into his digestive tract excess secretions that had a corroding effect on the walls of his stomach—bodily reactions related to situational stress on the one side and to physical debility on the other. In this instance the proof was possible because of Tom's physical abnormality (the tube to his stomach), but in many cases the internal processes must be mere guesswork.

In clinical attempts to study the interconnections between situational stresses and the physical complaints of patients, the more perplexing problems are of the latter type, complex and slow in development, indirect and almost imperceptible in genesis and effects. The sufferers generally portray in a vague way certain long-standing and chronic conflicts, socially derived, which have called forth constant and habituated reaction patterns that turn out to be physically inappropriate and penalizing in one or another respect. The crucial issue, of course, is to learn how to identify and correlate in a lucid way such sociological components with their biological complications.[2]

[1] Wolf, Stewart, and H. G. Wolff, *Human Gastric Function*, 1947.

[2] For representative discussions of this problem, see: Crew, F. A. E., "Social Medicine," 1944; Dark, E. P., "Sociological Medicine," 1945; Florence, P. S., "Social Medicine Based on Social Statistics," 1944; Freed, L. F., "Philosophy of Sociological Medicine," 1948; Minot, G. R., "Medical Social Aspects in Practice," 1934; Thornton, Janet, and Marjorie Knauth, *The Social Component in Medical Care*, 1937; Weiss, Edward, and O. S. English, *Psychosomatic Medicine*, 1949; Wofinden, R. C., "The Modern Trend in Social Medicine in the Home and in Industry," 1950.

Cultural or Subcultural Relativity

One concept of importance here is that of *cultural or subcultural relativity*, or the fact that different groups as a matter of course have variable definitions of similar or even of identical situations. A given situation that is cued to call forth strong emotional states and pronounced reactions in one sociocultural setting may as readily evoke only casual concern or amusement in another. Thus, definitions vary widely from group to group with respect to such matters as: the importance of economic status; the sacredness of property rights or debts; the guilt to be associated with tabooed acts; the significance of personal invectives, such as nicknames, curses, or the casting of magic spells; the meaning imputed to dreams; the implications of certain disease symptoms; and the labels given to or the feeling evoked by countless other situations common to man. In both therapy and research, therefore, it will be important to know to which groups and subgroups the patient or subject belongs, how frequently the culturally defined stressful situation appears in his life, and the extent to which he reacts in accord with the expectations of his groups.

It is frequently possible among ailing patients in clinical settings to find at one type-extreme the circumspect and nearly model member of his society or subgroup, a genuine creature of his culture, who strives diligently for prescribed goals, correctly identifies the social imperatives for his life, and pursues patterns of response to realistic situations in a manner that is certainly beyond reproach. It may also be apparent to the clinician that the patient is doing all this under a "nose-to-the-grindstone" regimen that is taking an exorbitant and debilitating toll in the physical misuse or even abuse of some parts of his body. He is thereby, and in an odd sense, "sick unto perfection," and may fulfill the folk-saying that "the good die young."

Two conclusions emerge from the discussion thus far. First, when cultures define some situations as being stressful and thus to be reacted to with crisis-like mobilization of resources, most of the successfully socialized members of the group will respond appropriately. But if these stress-laden situations, as defined by the culture, are frequently encountered by the members in the course of their group life, the culture itself is an important factor in initiating and demanding perdurable bodily reactions that are inept in the long run. The second conclusion is that some well-socialized members of a group, merely by paying strict attention to group demands even in culturally nonstressful situations, may acquire perdurable reaction patterns that are inept and end in illness. Thus, the cultural components in the linkage between situations and stress must always be clearly recognized.

This relationship between the situationally engendered stress in a particular individual and his physiological reactions is further complicated by a person's *own* peculiar, and perhaps idiosyncratic, definition of what is taking place, especially when it deviates significantly from the conventional labeling. Clinicians will often find, at the other type-extreme from the creature of culture, the socially deviant individual who also strives, although perhaps unconsciously, for "wayward" goals and who follows his own atypical and partly false clues in response to his life situation. His adaptations are out of harmony with socially approved behavior, as well as inappropriate on a physical basis. Under such circumstances social penalties are added to the physical injuries and stress may be compounded in a kind of "vicious cycle," for the more the subject reacts the worse becomes his plight. Following his false clues, he simultaneously impairs his body and his social relationships, perhaps even alienating the very persons best qualified to help and support him, and whose rejection leads to further deviations.

Between the two type-extremes just mentioned are many persons who are neither the direct victims of their culture nor pronounced social deviants. They are, if anything, their own victims within particular sociocultural settings. For them, the alerting signals that set off protective reaction patterns in a series of situations are mainly *symbolic* and without any necessary corresponding social or physical reality.[1]

In social context, symbolic cues can and do, of course, carry some real and some unrealistic threats of danger; and the individual finds himself in dilemmas where he must try to discriminate and interpret, with calculated risk, the critical cues for his conduct. This was the issue in the case of Tom, for his response (holding the hot liquid in his mouth) was cued more by the potential threat of his mother's wrath (an internalized symbolic cue) than by the painful reality of scalding tissue. The widespread use and function of symbolic cues in social relationships makes the individual potentially subject to a limitless range of threatening elements in similar situations, each of which may or may not involve realistic dangers. In all likelihood Tom's mother would have preferred the soiled floor and the consequent labor of cleaning it to the drastic consequences of his withholding action; that is, Tom's choice was based on an unrealistic symbolism. The point to be made, however, is that symbolic threats, whether realistic or not, can and do become stress-laden and response-driven for particular persons.

It is entirely possible, and not infrequently the case, that the highly personalized, symbolic goals or dangers for a person come to dominate and override many of the realistic directives for his life. These alerting and compelling signals can render major portions of his overt behavior and bodily responses grossly inappropriate. In such a predicament an individual may "react himself into distress" simultaneously on all three fronts of his individual-environmental relationship, cultural, social, and physical. Such a plight was summed up neatly by the patient who complained, "I have faced and suffered many

[1] Cassirer, Ernst, *An Essay on Man*, 1944; Chapin, F. S., "Latent Culture Patterns of the Unseen World of Social Reality," 1934.

troubles from all sides and for a long time; and the funny part is that most of these troubles never really happened. But here I am, sick in spirit, mind, and body, and feeling like I haven't got a friend in the world." Another patient somewhat less clearly stated, "I have died a thousand deaths already, and still I lie here, half alive."

Under such uniquely personalized states of symbolic and unrealistic sensitivity with a build-up of inappropriate reaction patterns, some individuals are constantly "crossing the bridge" before they reach it; and the wretched conditions of their bodies would indicate that they have already *crossed* many of these bridges. In substance, the symbolic threats bebecome *reified* by them and for them in their bodies.

Thus far, then, we have tried to indicate in a general way the relationships between cultural and personal definitions of situations and the appearance of stress. Now the task is to attempt to supply some more specific conceptual links between situation and stress.

Personality Typing and Attitude Conditioning

There are from the social sciences two leading formulations: the concepts of *personality typing* and *attitude conditioning*. They are not contradictory, though they are different in approach and emphasis. In general, contemporary anthropology has pursued and emphasized the former, while sociology and social psychology have given more attention to the latter. Perhaps psychiatry and the several schools of psychoanalysis have helped to integrate the two.

As noted earlier,[1] the conviction has long existed and recently grown among many clinicians that further illumination of the problems of linking situation with stress lies in the systematic exploration of the claim that the patient is first and foremost a *person* experiencing illness in his own characteristic way and that his behavior in stressful situations, whether by

[1] See Chapter 2.

overt actions or internal bodily reactions, can be understood best on this basis. Some would thus "lump the links" and go on to assume that all the connections between stress-evoking situations and structural changes can be clarified by a study of the subject as a *personality*.[1] When the processes and sequences are spelled out on this basis, the personality formulation implies that certain life situations evoke special stresses that elicit particular reaction patterns resulting in structural changes because of the type of personality involved. Thus, continuity throughout the chain of sequences, and the sociosomatic dynamics behind the illness, may be explained in terms of the "total personality." That becomes the critical variable for the wide-span or multi-steps in the sequences, and thus clarification and control would seem to rest primarily on knowledge of the personality and some capacity to change the personality. With respect to therapy for the *person*, this has led not infrequently to what resembles "cure-all" perscriptions and procedures on the one hand, or an attitude of fatalism and non-interference on the other. And with respect to therapy for the *organism*, it has sometimes induced the use of procedures of a "fix it" or "patch up the organ" nature that are directed to the ailing parts of the body; or it has led to more radical alterations, even to elimination of the ineptly performing parts.

This general point of view has led, perhaps as a short-cut, to manifold constructions of personality *types* or *profiles*, on

[1] For illustrations of this approach, see: Dunbar, H. F., *Synopsis of Psychosomatic Diagnosis and Treatment*, 1948; Gantt, W. H., "Principles of Nervous Breakdown—Schizokinesis and Autokinesis," 1953; Gildea, E. F., "Special Features of Personality Which Are Common to Certain Psychosomatic Disorders," 1949; Ham, G. C., and others, "Dynamic Aspects of the Personality Features and Reactions Characteristic of Patients with Graves' Disease," 1950; Horst, Paul, *The Prediction of Personal Adjustment*, 1941; Hunt, J. McV., editor, *Personality and the Behavior Disorders*, 1944; Kahn, Eugen, "Some Aspects of the Normal Personality Experiencing Disease," 1941; Kuntz, Albert, *Visceral Innervation and Its Relation to Personality*, 1951; Prichard, J. S., and others, "Effects of Stress and Results of Medication in Different Personalities with Parkinson's Disease," 1951; Redlich, F. C., "The Concept of Normality," 1952; Rogers, C. R., "Some Observations on the Organization of Personality," 1947.

either biological or sociological foundations, that may be correlated with the categories of situational factors on the one hand and the disease syndromes on the other.

In addition to clinicians, many students of the social sciences, especially in anthropology when allied with psychology or psychiatry, have been strongly influenced by the potentialities of the personality formulation. They are also making their own contributions to it, particularly through the use of life-history materials and various psychological tests for comparative studies of different cultural and subcultural patterns and their impact upon personal adjustments.[1] Further examples are also found in the works of sociologists and social psychologists in their study of the influence of different forms of family structure, or the organized relationships of other subgroupings and the ways they condition personality developments.[2]

[1] See, for example, Angyal, András, *Foundations for a Science of Personality*, 1941; Barnouw, Victor, *Acculturation and Personality Among the Wisconsin Chippewa*, 1950; Bateson, Gregory, "Cultural Determinants of Personality," 1944; Coutu, Walter, *Emergent Human Nature*, 1949; Dai, Bingham, "Personality Problems in Chinese Culture," 1941; Devereux, George, "The Logical Foundations of Culture and Personality Studies," 1945; *Idem*, "Areal Culture Pattern and Areal Basic Personality," 1951; *Idem*, "Mohave Culture and Personality," 1939; Gillin, John, and Victor Raimy, "Acculturation and Personality," 1940; Goldfrank, E. S., "Socialization, Personality, and the Structure of Pueblo Society," 1945; Hallowell, A. I., "Personality Structure and the Evolution of Man," 1950; Honigmann, J. J., *Culture and Ethos of Kaska Society*, 1949; Kardiner, Abram, "The Concept of Basic Personality Structure as an Operational Tool in the Social Sciences," 1945; Kluckhohn, Clyde, "Personality in Culture," 1949; Kluckhohn, Clyde, and O. H. Mowrer, "Culture and Personality," 1944; Kluckhohn, Clyde, and H. A. Murray, editors, *Personality in Nature, Society, and Culture*, 1948; Lewin, Kurt, *A Dynamic Theory of Personality*, 1935; Linton, Ralph, *Cultural Background of Personality*, 1945; *Idem*, "Problems of Status Personality," 1949; Mead, Margaret, "The Use of Primitive Material in the Study of Personality," 1935; Murray, H. A., *Explorations in Personality*, 1938; Plant, J. S., *Personality and the Cultural Pattern*, 1937; Sapir, Edward, "Personality," 1934; *Idem*, "The Emergence of the Concept of Personality in a Study of Cultures," 1934; Sargent, S. S., and M. W. Smith, editors, *Culture and Personality*, 1949.

[2] Ackerman, N. W., "'Social Role' and Total Personality," 1951; Adorno, T. W., and others, *The Authoritarian Personality*, 1950; Bennett, J. W., "Culture Change and Personality in a Rural Society," 1944; Brown, G. G., "Culture, Society, and Personality," 1951; Goldhamer, Herbert, "Recent Development in Personality Studies," 1948; Gough, H. G., "A New Dimension of Status," 1948; Havighurst, R. J., and Hilda Taba, *Adolescent Character and Personality*, 1949; Klineberg, Otto, "A Science of National Character," 1944; Krout, M. H., and

We subscribe to the over-all personality formulation with recognition of its promise for future developments and also with certain reservations. It does provide what appears to be a significant conceptual linkage of the psychosocial and biophysical dynamics in man's experience of disease, and future research may illuminate its relevance for this problem. It seems to us, however, that too little specificity and agreement have been reached in our current formulations of personality to make them very useful in solving clinical or theoretical problems.[1]

To be sure, certain attributed characteristics or types of personality are associated with particular diseases. For example, one may describe the typical gastric-ulcer patient as a person longing for affection and support but putting up a false front of independence. The person with ulcerative colitis is judged, as a rule, to be hopeless and inarticulate; the sufferer from migraine headaches, a driving, perfectionistic, intellectual worker. However, since there are many instances of individuals falling outside of, rather than within, such descriptive categories, these "personality profiles" seem often to confuse rather than clarify the issues and to overlook important

---

Ross Stagner, "Personality Development in Radicals," 1939; Lindesmith, A. R., and A. L. Strauss, "A Critique of Culture-Personality Writings," 1950; Merton, R. K., "Bureaucratic Structure and Personality," 1940; Parsons, Talcott, "Personality and Social Structure," 1951; Stanton, A. H., and S. E. Perry, editors, *Personality and Political Crisis*, 1951; Thomas, W. I., "The Configurations of Personality," 1928; Underwood, F. W., and Irma Honigmann, "A Comparison of Socialization and Personality in Two Simple Societies," 1947; Winch, R. F., "The Study of Personality in the Family Setting," 1950; Woodard, J. W., "The Relation of Personality Structure to the Structure of Culture," 1938.

[1] For a discussion of testing techniques in the typing and assessment of personality, see, for example: Bell, J. E., *Projective Techniques*, 1948; Benedek, Therese, *Insight and Personality Adjustment*, 1946; Blake, R. R., and G. V. Ramsey, editors, *Perception:* An Approach to Personality, 1951; Billig, Otto, and others, "Aspects of Personality and Culture in a Guatemalan Community," 1947–1948; Cattell, R. B., *Description and Measurement of Personality*, 1946; DuBois, C. A., *The People of Alor*, 1944; Ferguson, L. W., *Personality Measurement*, 1952; Henry, W. E., "The Thematic Apperception Technique in the Study of Culture-Personality Relations," 1947; Mowrer, O. H., *Learning Theory and Personality Dynamics*, 1950; Sargent, Helen, "Projective Methods: Their Origins, Theory, and Application," 1945.

connections in the chain of events. In general, the research that has aimed to correlate such personality typings with the specific situations, stresses, reaction patterns, and disease syndromes has yielded rather modest contributions.[1]

The same generalization can be made, incidentally, for the contemporary anthropological formulations that attempt to correlate cultural "patterns" with personality "structures," "modes," or types. There is doubtless some basis for this, but it is essentially another typological approach that has not yet advanced to a degree of specificity or refinement that takes us much beyond gross and blurred categorization or net impressions.

It may be observed at this point that a methodological pitfall is possibly present in the assemblage, analysis, and formulations of the data around the concept of personality as the comprehensive intervening variable between situations and end results in the individual's adaptations. Not seldom a clinician assumes that a full description of the signs and symptoms of a patient's illness gives him sufficient data for predicting the "personality type" represented by the patient without having seen him. Likewise, specialists in "culture-personality" studies imply that a full knowledge of the culture is sufficient for portrayal of the "modes" or types of the representative "bearers of the culture" in the given society, or vice versa. Since the patients are the persons whose personalities are represented in the clinical cases and the cultural informants are usually the personalities represented in the culture-personality studies, and without independent controls, the predictive capacity in both cases may rest essentially on little more than the necessary experience required to predict the reverse side of a coin when the expert has become familiar with samples of that particular coin; for example, a Buffalo nickel. The performance may explain nothing generically.

[1] Cobb, Stanley, "Patterns of Personality," 1950, pp. 183–196.

While granting the relevance and the possible implications of recent developments concerning personality in both the medical and social science fields, it would appear that these formulations are still too lacking in specificity adequately to bridge the gaps now existing in our understanding of the linkage of situational dynamics with disease processes. Accordingly, we have found it more helpful, although not entirely satisfactory, to adopt a somewhat more specific conceptualization with regard to the psychosocial aspects of protective reaction patterns. This is the concept of *attitude.*

Habituated Attitudes

Attitudes may be conveniently regarded as personal variables intervening between stimulus situations on the one hand and emergent responses on the other. It is assumed that their formation is conditioned both by the constitutional make-up of the individual and his previous life experience, resulting in a set of predispositions to respond in a specific way at a given time to certain situations. Presumably over a period of time individuals come to possess a fund of attitudes, or particular organizations of attitudes, that recur in repetitive situations and that provide characteristic behavioral responses. Until we have a better formulation, we suggest that these *habituated attitudes* constitute the linkage between the situational stimuli evoking stressful states and the reaction patterns that may prove inept for the organism.

Attitudes, as we use the term, should be analyzed in greater detail, calling attention to those dimensions of the concept, and their interrelations and implications, most pertinent to our present concern. The three major dimensions of importance are *scope*, *direction*, and *intensity*. The "scope" dimension distinguishes between *general* and *specific* attitudes; by "direction" is meant *positive* or *negative*, *favorable* or *unfavorable;* and by "intensity" is meant the *strength* with which a given attitude is held. Without attempting to go into the full ramifications of a theory of attitudes, the relevance of these conceptions to the problem at hand may be briefly indicated.[1]

Let us assume that a physician has reason to suspect that the root of a given patient's ailments is to be found in his family relationships. This has been established, let us say, by implicit information offered by the patient and also by some tentative correlations between the patient's symptoms and fluctuations in his relationships at home. With this general clue, the physician wishes to study the more specific links between the general family situation and the patient's symptoms. The conceptual tools, provided by the analysis of attitudes, will be very helpful. Thus, for example, the physician can explore the *scope* and *direction* of the patient's attitudes toward his family; that is, whether they are directed, favorably or unfavorably, toward the general status of the family (in contrast to other families or to the patient's hopes of what its status would be) or toward specific members who have not been living up to their responsibilities. In a similar manner, the physician can probe the *strength* of the attitudes thus revealed, keeping in mind that weak, favorable attitudes result in practical indifference toward their objects and if weakened further may even reverse direction and become unfavorable.[2]

[1] See Wolff, H. G., *Stress and Disease*, 1953, pp. 128–139. For a sampling of the writings on attitudes, consult: Allport, G. W., "Attitudes," 1935; Bonner, Hubert, "Attitudes and Behavior," 1953; Droba, D. D., "The Nature of Attitude," 1933; Dunham, H. W., "Topical Summaries of Current Literature: Social Attitudes," 1940; Faris, Ellsworth, "The Concept of Social Attitudes," 1925; *Idem*, "Attitudes and Behavior," 1928; Grace, W. J., and D. T. Graham, "Relationship of Specific Attitudes and Emotions to Certain Bodily Diseases," 1952; Kelley, H. H., and E. H. Volkart, "The Resistance to Change of Group Anchored Attitudes," 1952; Kempf, E. J., "The Law of Attitude," 1945; La Piere, R. T., "The Sociological Significance of Measurable Attitudes," 1938; Lee, A. M., "Sociological Theory in Public Opinion and Attitude Studies," 1947; McNemar, Quinn, "Opinion-Attitude Methodology," 1946; Newcomb, T. M.. "Community Roles in Attitude Formation," 1942; Strauss, A. L., "The Concept of Attitude in Social Psychology," 1945; Thompson, L. M., "Attitudes and Acculturation," 1948.

[2] For further reports on research in attitudes, see: Bain, Read, "An Attitude on Attitude Research," 1928; *Idem*, "Theory and Measurement of Attitudes and Opinions," 1930; DuBois, C. A., "Attitudes Toward Food and Hunger in Alor," 1941; Hatt, Paul, "Class and Ethnic Attitudes," 1948; Hu, Hsien-Chin, "The

The exploration of these dimensions of attitudes has considerable significance for understanding the linkage between situation and stress. For example, a very strong, favorable attitude on the part of a person toward one member of his family, without a corresponding favorable attitude toward the family generally or its other significant members, may well provide, in a sociocultural setting, the bases of internal conflict that precipitate and perpetuate inept bodily responses. Or in a cultural setting, where the expectation is that persons in a certain category (parents, for example) will have attitudes of a certain scope, direction, and strength toward persons in another category (their parents or their children), and where such attitudes are lacking as a consequence of life experiences, we again have the conditions that mediate between situation and stress.

In more general terms, our formulation suggests that knowledge of these dimensions of a person's attitudes reveals the *emotional* and *motivational* components or attitudinal "sets" which color, and condition, behavioral responses. Here, our assumption is that we must always *infer* attitudes, motives, and emotional states from certain external indications, but that attitudinal dimensions lie nearer the surface than the other two, hence, can be more readily inferred, thus providing clues to the underlying dynamics. Let us briefly discuss emotions and motives as these relate to attitudinal sets.

Central to the concept of attitudes are the emotional components. Currently the word "emotion" is confined mainly to those states, conscious or unconscious, that reach sufficient intensity in an identifiable direction as to elicit readily perceptible manifestations of mood or feeling-tone as associated with either overt behavior or internal bodily reactions. Fear or anger of different degrees, with corresponding bodily

---

Chinese Concepts of 'Face,'" 1944; Newcomb, T. M., and George Svehla, "Intra-family Relationships in Attitude," 1937; Sanai, Mahmoud, "An Experimental Study of Social Attitudes," 1951; Thurstone, L. L., and E. J. Chave, *The Measurement of Attitude*, 1929.

changes and with attack or retreat as the behavioral correlates of attitudinal directions, are familiar examples. Indeed, it is probable that pure nonemotional responses are very rare, for events and stimuli generally evoke phenomena of orientation even though they may be promptly perceived as being of such minor significance as to call for only minimal adjustments. Thus, the analysis of psychosocial dynamics in illness must proceed, not in terms of the absence or presence of emotional components, but in terms of the amount or degree of emotional involvement of the person.[1]

It must be remembered, however, that such emotional states as are generally labeled "fear" or "anger," are much more complex than the simple terminology would suggest. Because of their great variety and range, they are often too subtle to detect, and many emotional states as yet have no labels. Moreover, those paired attitudinal opposites, called "ambivalence" by the psychoanalyst, with their emotional ramifications also resist easy interpretation and require much more study before their relations to illness can be clearly understood.

On the other hand, it is a striking fact that for a particular individual the bodily reactions evoked during typically stressful situations have a high degree of specificity and recurrence. Although there exists a wide range of possible "attitudinal sets" in terms of emotional manifestations, an individual during stress usually centers upon relatively few, or perhaps only one, which he elaborates, intensifies, and overworks. One person may tend to respond typically to stress by way of aggression, another by way of rage, still another by anxiety,

[1] For representative material on emotions, consult: Brown, J. S., and I. E. Farber, "Emotions Conceptualized as Intervening Variables," 1951; Cannon, W. B., "The Role of Emotion in Disease," 1936; Cobb, Stanley, *Emotions and Clinical Medicine*, 1950; Devereux, George, "Social Structure and the Economy of Affective Bonds," 1942; LaBarre, Weston, "The Cultural Basis of Emotions and Gestures," 1947; Linton, Ralph, "The Effects of Culture on Mental and Emotional Processes," 1939; Maier, N. R. F., *Frustration:* The Study of Behavior Without a Goal, 1949; Romano, John, "Emotional Components of Illness," 1943; Saul, L. J., *Emotional Maturity*, 1947; Sheldon, W. H., *Varieties of Temperament*, 1942; Young, P. T., *Emotion in Man and Animal*, 1943.

thus making the core of his emotional components relatively easy to trace throughout long periods of his life. In short, the critical role of emotions in physiological processes is well known, even though their range, variety, and corresponding effects are not yet plotted in detail.

Another area to be explored is the relationship between attitudes and motivation. On the one hand, it would seem that motives vary independently of attitudinal sets, frequently perhaps being the sources of attitudes. If, for example, a person is strongly motivated to achieve a given goal, this motive-strength may well be a conditioning factor in the appearance of attitudes relating to objects or persons that either impede or promote the attainment of the goal. On the other hand, attitudes of given scope, direction, and intensity, especially very strong attitudes, may operate as motives in their own right. Strong positive attitudes toward mother or father (as emphasized by the psychoanalysts, for example) can undoubtedly behave as motives in certain acts relating to the objects of these attitudes.

In this connection, of course, it should be recalled that there are different levels of awareness with regard to motives. It is now generally agreed that but a small fraction of the conditioning experiences of the individual enters or remains in full consciousness, many of his reactions to stimuli being the consequence of partly forgotten or unconscious motives. It is possible, for example, for one to manifest feelings of resentment and at the same time sincerely protest any awareness of it. Observations on the gastric mucosa of the patient, Tom, revealed that the burden of conflict having the greatest significance, or bearing the greatest threat for him, was actually the one most relevant to the changes that occurred in his stomach, regardless of how conscious he appeared to be of it. Since major conflicts are more likely to be repressed than minor ones, as perceived by the individual, the greater significance of those of which the individual is least aware is often confirmed.

When propelled by unconscious motivations, of course, the individual is at a loss to know what to do about the stresses on a voluntary basis, and the autonomic and involuntary processes run their course. Experimental study of the latter therefore often provides a more reliable index of the stress potentials in his life, and his attitudes toward them, than the information he is able to impart—except perhaps during elaborate and prolonged periods of self-revelation, as in the case of psychoanalysis. It does not *necessarily* follow, however, that verbal reports of attitudes are always unreliable or that they generally contradict the behavioral responses experimentally observed. Thus, from the standpoint of method it is usually desirable to supplement each type of information, verbal and experimental, with the other.[1]

Returning now to our central problem, that of the first linkage between typical situation and specified stress, the significance of this discussion can be summarized. Having acquired a fund of attitudes of specified scope, direction, and strength in the course of his life experience, the person is potentially ready to respond to situations that contain environmental objects, including events and other persons. He is characterized by a particular *organization* of attitudes, an attitudinal system as it were, that relates him to the situation. This means that attention is differentially directed toward the different aspects of the situation, selecting and emphasizing some, ignoring or minimizing others. Attitudes, in short, are preconditions of that process we have previously referred to as the "definition of the situation." In interaction with the properties of the situation, they set off a chain of events involving

[1] For elaborations on the concept of motivation, see: Foote, N. N., "Identification as the Basis for a Theory of Motivation," 1951; Hilgard, E. R., "Human Motives and the Concept of the Self," 1949; Kuo, Z. Y., "The Genesis of the Cat's Response to the Rat," 1930; Maslow, A. H., "A Theory of Human Motivation," 1943; *Idem*, "Self-Actualizing People: A Study of Psychological Health," 1950; Morgan, C. T., *Physiological Psychology*, 1943; Seligman, C. G., "The Unconscious in Relation to Anthropology," 1928; Sinnott, E. W., *Cell and Psyche*, 1950; *Idem*, "The Biology of Purpose," 1952.

perception, cognition, and judgment, resulting in "an *interpretation* or *point of view*, and eventually in a policy and a behavior pattern."[1] Situation and stress, then, are linked by means of a "definition" derived in part from the reality of the situation and in part from the fund of habituated attitudes brought to the situation by the person.

Once a situation is defined as stressful, however, the emotional and motivational components of attitudes provide the link between specified stress and protective reaction patterns. A stressful situation requires more than "minimal adjustment"; it requires a mobilization of bodily resources that will be sufficient to carry the person through the stress. Thus, if the attitudinal set consists of strong attitudes, extreme in direction, emotional states are touched off that link up with the heightened physiological reactions of the autonomic nervous system. And if the situations defined as stressful appear frequently, or if the person overgeneralizes from certain specific situations to many general situations, the protective reaction patterns set off by the emotional components of attitudes can be overworked or ill-used, with possible consequences of functional disorders and perhaps structural changes in the affected organs.

From this standpoint, we might reformulate our original sequential chain to read as follows: motive → habituated attitude → situation → definition of situation → specified stress → emotional states → bodily reactions of a protective variety. In brief, if we regard man as a goal-striving or motivated creature, with emotional components in all his responses, those situations that evoke strong emotional correlates to behavioral responses inevitably affect the bodily processes because of the tie between emotions and physiological performance.

When we see that the situational threats for an individual are multiple, complex, and highly variable, however, still another problem is raised: why is it that particular persons suffer from one ailment rather than another? Stanley Cobb

[1] Thomas, W. I., *Social Behavior and Personality*, 1951, p. 107.

has underlined this "problem of specificity" as one of the most difficult aspects of our approach to the whole field of psychosocial dynamics in disease. Cobb observes that "innumerable clinical observations indicate that emotional stress may cause dysfunction and eventually, in some cases, lesions of an organ. But the reason why one vomits, another palpitates, and another has hives is unknown."[1] We cannot, of course, pretend to have any answers to this problem, but it is well within our purpose to spell out the problem and suggest a possible approach.

The Problem of Specificity

There are, in reality, three aspects of the "problem of specificity" that challenge our attention. On the one hand, within what may be regarded as similar stress-evoking situations, some persons are found manifesting little or no stress and others, who do show stress, may respond with different sets of reaction patterns and perhaps also with correspondingly different symptoms. To similar types of situations, for example, we have seen that some individuals respond "normally" while others react ineptly as organisms by the use and abuse of their nasal or visual organs, others by overeating or by excessive physiological preparations for eating, others by misapplied reactions within their gastrointestinal tracts, others by overwork of their skeletal muscles and cranial arteries, and still others by pronounced fluctuations in their cardiovascular systems or by change in metabolic rates, and so on. This aspect, in short, is concerned with the fact that persons often reveal typical, recurring symptoms in response to all types of stressful situations.

A second aspect of the "problem of specificity" is to be found in the fact that the same person may respond to his typically stressful situations with mixed or alternating reaction patterns. Thus, when first presented, such a situation may represent one kind of threat and call forth a certain pat-

[1] Cobb, Stanley, *Emotions and Clinical Medicine*, 1950, p. 197.

tern of adaptation and yet, when it has persisted and is perceived later on, may evoke quite another. Thus, for example, people may react to the same life stress with alternating constipation and diarrhea. There may, moreover, be periods of mixed and alternating patterns with apparent corresponding changes in the meaning of the situations. Gastric hyperfunction as exhibited by gastric hyperacidity, increased contraction, and decreased emptying time is often linked with constipation, even in the case of peptic ulceration. The "dogged," persistent, aggressive pattern of behavior is similar, although there seems to be more anger mixed with the anxieties of the patient with peptic ulcer. On the other hand, vomiting and diarrhea are more commonly linked, and characteristically occur in a setting of being "shocked," "disgusted," stunned by bad news, or confronted by sudden death or tragedy. The fact that constipation and diarrhea alternate in the same individual has been commonly noted, and may imply that the pattern of "grimly hanging on" cannot be sustained. At intervals, it seems, the patient is overwhelmed and "lets go" despite himself, and thus constipation gives way to episodes of diarrhea. From the standpoint of the present formulations, it might be interesting to study these cases of alternating responses in connection with the aforementioned attitudinal ambivalence.

The third aspect of "specificity" has to do with apparent reversals of symptoms. An apparently very frustrating situation may come to have for the individual a countereffect, actually resulting in a reduction of the intensity of his stress and his reactions to it. The situation may no longer be pertinent to his previous strivings, or his position appears hopeless or untenable to him. Stock examples come out of our common knowledge of persons who "take in their stride" threats that have reached stages of catastrophe or despair; while they fret, chafe, and over-react to what appears to the observer as relatively minor difficulties. In effect, they seem to "strain at gnats and swallow camels."

It has been observed that reaction patterns growing out of stress and bearing upon illness may be interrupted, with consequent diminution of the symptoms, when the life situations of the sufferer change radically, even if for the worse. An interesting example is reported by Groen[1] who had treated a number of Amsterdam Jewish patients for ulcers before, during, and following World War II. Most of them were prominent persons who had acquired ulcers under relatively comfortable standards of living but in highly competitive business and professional careers. Dr. Groen followed them into the concentration camps where their former goals appeared hopeless, but where they suffered severe deprivations, indignities, and actual danger, not knowing from day to day whether they would survive. The new threats and stresses, objectively defined, were far greater than the former ones; but, oddly enough the majority lost their ulcer symptoms while in the concentration camp. With their former goals appearing hopeless, they gave up striving for them and seemed no longer in the old sense "ambitious." They then concerned themselves with the barest necessities of life and bickered about little things, considering the attainment of slight comforts major triumphs and giving vent to petty hostilities. In most instances it appeared that the men's wives were providing them with more emotional support than formerly. Later, however, when the harrowing camp experience was behind them and they had returned to their old way of life and professional or business pursuits, the peptic ulcer complaints recurred.

Observations of a similar kind have been made concerning a group of missionaries in the Far East who were incarcerated in Japanese camps. These persons previously suffered from migraine headache but were free from it while in camp, although they were forced to suffer deprivations and undergo a certain degree of torture. Thus, great stress may be experi-

[1] Groen, Jacques, *De Psychopathogenese van het Ulcus Ventriculi et Duodeni*, 1947; *Idem*, "Psychogenesis and Psychotherapy of Ulcerative Colitis," 1947.

enced by individuals without evoking the particular reaction patterns which normally accompany stress.[1]

These three aspects of the problem of specificity spell out in more detail the crucial problems of the second linkage in our general sequential formulation, that between specified stress and particular reaction pattern. It would be fanciful to assume that we are very close to solving them in a systematic, scientific fashion. For the moment these problems must be handled, it seems to us, in terms very similar to the general viewpoint of this volume—by a technique that closely resembles the life-history approach. The validity of this is indicated by the following considerations.

Limitations in Adaptation

It seems clear that the types of adaptation of which the organism is capable have definite limits, while the potential variations in the stress-evoking situations, especially in their social and cultural complexities, are limitless. The organs with which an individual may react to stress are limited in number, and so are the types of malfunctioning which any organ may exhibit. Similar limits exist on the specific foci of tissue damage or other defects, and on the symptom formations to be found. Man's body, in short, is finite in organ structure and response potentials, while the varieties and complexities of his environmental situations and their implications for stress are probably infinite, especially when the possible shades of symbolic meanings are added. The individual is bound, therefore, to respond in similar or identical ways and with the same organs or systems of organs to a variety of situations and threats. Likewise, the ill effects may be correspondingly similar. Thus, as a member of society and as a person in a culture, the individual's exposures to stress are practically unlimited; but as an organism, he is subject to a "principle of limited possibilities." This fact alone makes it highly pertinent in any study of stress asso-

[1] Wolff, H. G., *Stress and Disease*, 1953, pp. 121–122.

ciated with illness to know the intimate and relevant details of a person's previously conditioned attitudes that may link the situational stimuli to the particular reaction patterns.

To us, moreover, it may not be so much a question of why one organ instead of another becomes pathologically involved during stress, but of how any organ is implicated in a pattern of inept responses to stress-laden situations. It is probably too simple a formulation, and perhaps a misleading one, to assume that stress strikes the weakest organ or the weakest link in the organ system, as was believed for so long. Recent investigations have pointed toward a new supposition: that a strong and well-functioning organ or system of organs may be called upon initially, and may thereafter bear the brunt of other deficiencies of the body; and be overworked for so long a period in protecting the weaker portions that they are the ones that break down or develop lesions.

As a result of accumulating studies we would subscribe to the hypothesis that it is, indeed, not the constitutional inferiority of the organ that leads to its choice in such a pattern of response, but rather the total dynamics of the situation in which the individual is involved, and his attitude toward it, as determined in large part by his personal history. The particular protective reaction pattern evoked and perpetuated may be seen as a function of the significance of the stress-laden events to the individual in relationship to his goals, his habituated attitudes, and his particular sociocultural backgrounds.

Such a formulation seems to resolve some of the problems associated with the fact of limited responses to the unlimited stress potentials and ties in well with the variables involved in different definitions of the situation. It provides some perspective for understanding the characteristic bodily reactions of the same person to different stressful situations; the mixed, alternating responses of a person to the same situation; and the shifts in long-established protective reaction patterns when the stressful situation is dramatically altered. These data "fall into place," exhibit a pattern, when it is considered that the autonomic nervous system is restricted in the kinds of responses it can manifest; that it responds and complies with signals defined by emotional states; and that the source of the signals lies in the psychosocial definitions of situations. As the signals, or meanings, change, so within limits do the autonomic responses, thus continuing to perform "to the best of their ability."

From this viewpoint, a critical and provocative issue emerges, however. It is the difference between conscious and unconscious motivations and how changes in them may affect attitudes. It may be that conscious motivations are modified by slight but perceptible changes in the threatening situation, while unconscious motivations with their accompanying protective reaction patterns are modified mainly by pronounced changes in the threatening situation that make the habituated reaction patterns grossly untenable as in the case of the missionaries who experienced relief from migraine headache when their positions and goal-strivings became entirely untenable. Does this imply, moreover, that the unconsciously motivated stresses are generally reached and dealt with from the situational side by gross and pronounced changes in existing life situations on the one hand, or by the painstaking and prolonged psychological methods that bring the stress-evoking situations into full consciousness and work through their untenable characteristics by degrees perceptively, emotionally, and motivationally, as in dynamically oriented therapy? What are the implications of such a theory for the analysis of stress-provoking situations and comprehensive patient care?

Summary

We propose the following tentative formulation concerning the nature of a protective reaction pattern and its relation to the life situation of the individual:

1. Regardless of the apparent magnitude of the stimulus situation, the capacity of a given stressful event to evoke

a protective reaction pattern depends upon its special significance to the individual involved.

2. The significance of a given stress-arousing situation for the individual, according to his physical capacities and previous conditioning experiences, determines the characteristics of the protective reaction evoked.
3. When an individual, exhibiting a given protective reaction pattern with coexisting symptoms, is confronted with a situation that, through its new and different meaning, evokes correspondingly different responses, the latter may so overshadow the former as to cause the symptoms to disappear temporarily.

As we have pointed out frequently in these pages, probably few medical or social scientists would challenge such an over-all view, which attempts to link man's physical ailments to his life experience as a member of society and a person in a culture. Yet some paradoxes remain. On the theoretical level there is the problem of the concept of adaptation, or adjustment, as it applies to apt and inept protective reaction patterns. It is easy for such a concept, however useful or even indispensable to broad theoretical formulations it may be, to appear to be another example of "circular reasoning." How does one know that a particular bodily response is adaptive? Because it is there. Why is it there? Because it is adaptive! Before we can truly say that the reaction patterns we have discussed are apt or inept, it is necessary to state on what grounds the judgment is made. Perhaps such criteria cannot be established for classes of people or whole populations, even within a specified sociocultural setting; but they can, no doubt, be established for given persons and typical situations within their life experiences. At least such an idea is worthy of further exploration from a medicosocial standpoint.

At the practical level of therapy this approach also creates problems. In terms of prevailing medical practice, routine therapeutic techniques, and the usual clinical facilities, it seems inapplicable, and no doubt the public is not yet able to appreciate or pay for such comprehensive care, however basic it may be to health and welfare. Yet, we have assumed throughout the discourse that our fundamental objective is the health and relatively continuous well-being of man as an organism, a member of society, and a person in a culture. We have attempted to show that with this objective it is possible to portray and clarify measurably how within a given environment individuals may develop inept protective reaction patterns in the pursuit of their goals. Such a perspective, linking sociological and biological dynamics in the experience of illness, provides significant glimpses of a new vista in medical care.

Now we can begin to know the price we pay in illness for a given way of life. With the new knowledge obtainable, we may reduce the toll; or develop competence to deal more effectively with the hazards involved. Occasionally, we may conclude that as members of a given society and in particular life situations there are other things more important than physical comfort, and a few that are more to be sought after than health or even life itself. At any rate, man should welcome and profit by the opportunity to see and comprehend just what his goals and actions are costing him. He may choose to continue living as he has been; or, perchance, he may decide that his attitudes and his ways are poor, that he has been misled, trapped, and confused, and therefore attempt to change his goals and his pace.

CHAPTER 6

Hospital Practice in Social Science Perspective

A SYSTEMATIC STUDY of the network of human experiences that "trap" people into illness yields some insight on how structural changes characteristic of disease result from inept and misused patterns of response (overt behavior or internal bodily reactions). It further reveals how these protective reaction patterns are set off and intensified by stresses evoked in life situations that have become socioculturally staged and cued. The concept of *habituated attitudes* that become established with certain degrees of generalization and rigidity provides us with some knowledge concerning the connections between the wide-spanned and step-by-step linkage of situations at one end of the continuum with diseases at the other end.

On the basis of these formulations, we are now ready to conclude that medicine is potentially a social as well as a physical science and that successful medical practice depends on the former as on the latter disciplines.

It follows that even though extensive and precise physical findings are obtained and utilized in therapy, other critical elements operating in a person's experience of illness can profoundly influence the results. Moreover it is implied, that treatment of the physical components in an ailment may be largely irrelevant and misapplied if critical personal and social elements are neglected or incorrectly assayed. Still further, it would appear that without knowledge of what has been happening in the life of the patient as a person, there is danger in therapy of the activation and intensification of stresses similar to those that set off the habituated and ill-fated protective reaction patterns and that helped to produce the illness. In short, the disease under treatment can be made worse on psychosocial grounds even when therapy in the biophysical sphere is all that anyone could expect.

The same perspective on the problems of disease that leads to a searching interest in the psychological and social factors underlying specific complaints also awakens medical concern for the environmental forces that impinge upon the patient during the course of his illness. What occurs, for instance, within the family circle becomes important in the framework of medical care. Furthermore, the institutional or subgroup setting in which diagnosis and treatment take place calls for special study. Let us, therefore, briefly follow the patient into the medical center and consider some of the experiences that he may undergo.

An outstanding change in the practice of medicine in recent times has been the shift in context from home to hospital for the major phases of patient care. The credo of specialization, which requires precise procedures and more elaborate equipment, has led quite naturally to rapid and extensive development of the hospital as a suitable base for treatment of the sick and for the training of therapists. Concentration of research and medical education in the university center, for which the hospital was an essential unit, has helped to speed this expansion.

The many advantages of such a centralization of the site of treatment have become obvious. It has saved busy therapists much time formerly spent traveling from door to door. It has afforded medical staffs easier access to facilities and data, more effective research opportunities, and more frequent incentives and occasions for consultation with colleagues. Further, it has provided for greater standardization and systematization of procedures, and ensured far more effective control of the patient, his immediate environment, and the details of his therapy. Indeed, it would seem that many elements in the patient's indigenous environment could now be safely ignored, at least during the immediate phases of his treatment. Thus, in a sense, the tasks and responsibilities of the therapist have been simplified. The system provides him with an exceptional opportunity to share medical responsibility with a growing body of fellow professionals who carry weight and extra authority as specialists. He thus stands less alone in his professional activities and is reinforced by tremendous reserves. As has been true of the business corporation, the medical institution facilitates division of labor and diffuses as well as fortifies personal accountability. As in business, too, economic efficiencies are apparent in the concentration and coordination of facilities and services, at least within limits.

On the other hand, as we are coming to recognize, there are serious liabilities in this new treatment locale. While the physician profits by the specific economies and many "workshop" conveniences as contrasted with his horse-and-buggy days, the new system frequently disrupts his earlier more leisurely and personal contact with those under his supervision. Indeed, social distance between the physician and his patient at the hospital bedside has widened increasingly, with his professional services fractionated and his prestige established on a more remote pedestal. Moreover, contacts between the physician and the patient's family are greatly restricted and their relationship has undergone an even more profound cleavage.

Then, too, as we now see the situation, unexpected dangers lurk within the institutionalized setting for medical care. When large numbers of gravely ill persons with urgent needs are thus congregated, special risks, both physical and psychosocial, appear in treatment situations. Assembly-line methods increase the likelihood of oversights and make less feasible the orientation of patient care around the particular needs of the individual. For the sick person, sustaining links with his customary life are weakened or severed. A new environment has to be faced, which is in many respects threatening, especially since he is no longer expected or permitted to make many decisions for himself. Rather, he becomes subject to rules, regulations, and jurisdictions that are strange to him. He loses prerogatives and is pressed into compliance.

In addition, the patient usually finds within the institution itself an atmosphere of crisis and strain, compounded by the aggregation of fellow sufferers and not infrequently by the pressures and frustrations under which staff members perform their duties. New patterns of thought, attitude, and activities, which have the marks of a distinctive culture, can be sensed at least vaguely on every side. Specific staff-member attitudes toward patients, their problems, and their behavior are apparent and, though explainable in terms of the setup of the hospital system and the wear and tear on life there, they often tend to have a punitive effect upon the patient, sometimes adversely influencing the outcome of his illness. Resentments at this contrasting and seemingly "callous culture," and anxieties occasioned by loss of accustomed reinforcements common to family and community life, can easily complicate the patient's reactions, introducing new stress patterns for him or intensifying his old ones.

Potential Liabilities in Hospital Life

Medical policy related to hospital practice has long emphasized the manifold physical hazards consequent to a high concentration of patients, diseases, and technical equipment in treatment centers. Unless sanitary precautions and other measures are strictly observed, prevalent microbes may endanger the health of patients and staff members alike; and the complicated technical apparatus, if handled with anything less than expert knowledge and constant vigilance, threatens the lives it was designed to save. In the complex hospital setting, moreover, chance risks of various kinds are increased, such as those that result from careless transmittal or execution of doctors' orders, mislabeled medicines and misplaced instruments, ill-advised or poorly prepared meals, and the neglect of countless, seemingly small but crucial details. To reduce these dangers to a minimum, elaborate precautionary measures have been developed.

In contrast to the general recognition and detailed consideration of these physical dangers within the hospital setting, the social and emotional hazards inherent within the system have until recently received much less positive attention.[1] The realization is now growing, however, that the hospital embodies a social environment in which established procedures, distinctive attitudes, and structured interpersonal relationships exert powerful influences upon staff members and patients alike. It is also suspected that certain of the behavioral patterns, communicable attitudes, and stereotyped relationships, unless recognized and handled with care, can produce untold damage in treatment situations. Some of the personal relationships can become charged with exaggerated significance for the patient, so that his reactions, especially in the critical stages of his illness, may have decided effects upon his health and general welfare. The balance that exists, for example, in the patient's reactions to staff members between doubt and feelings of rejection, on the one hand, and trust and acceptance on the other, may often pivot on very fine points. And who can say just how often particular relationships tip the scales one way or the other in the course of an illness?

[1] There is an accumulating literature on this subject. Consult, for example: Caudill, William, and others, "Social Structure and Interaction Processes on a Psychiatric Ward," 1952; Clark, K. G., *Preventive Medicine in Medical Schools*, 1953; Commission on Hospital Care, *Hospital Care in the United States*, 1947; Devereux, George, "The Social Structure of the Hospital as a Factor in Total Therapy," 1949; *Idem*, "The Social Structure of a Schizophrenia Ward and Its Therapeutic Fitness," 1944; Devereux, George, and F. R. Weiner, "The Occupational Status of Nurses," 1950; Romano, John, "Patients' Attitudes and Behavior in Ward Round Teaching," 1941; Spence, J. C., *The Care of Children in Hospitals*, 1948; Stanton, A. H., and M. S. Schwartz, "Medical Opinion and the Social Context in the Mental Hospital," 1949; Tudor, G. E., "A Sociopsychiatric Nursing Approach to Intervention in a Problem of Mutual Withdrawal on a Mental Hospital Ward," 1952; Wessen, A. F., *The Social Structure of a Modern Hospital*, 1950; Whitehorn, J. C., and others, editors, *Psychiatry and Medical Education*, 1952.

Physicians have long been somewhat aware of the potential hazards in staff-patient relationships, and they have tried to limit the risk of any ill effects by the imposition of strict regulations, with the result that the hospital has become a uniquely and perhaps negatively controlled, and one might even say ritualized, social environment. In the absence of scientific knowledge of the mechanisms and dynamics involved, and lacking personnel adequately trained in these matters, the ever-present danger that sickness can be aggravated through the little understood social variables has probably justified a policy of neutralizing and ritualizing many of them in hospital practice.

More recently, however, the availability of better trained personnel, and the progressive development of research techniques and general knowledge in the social sciences, is making it possible to explore and formulate some of the more positive potentialities inherent in the hospital society. Consideration of these positive powers, rather than the negative, and utilization rather than neutralization of them in the interest of the patient's recovery and rehabilitation constitute newly emerging goals in medical care.

Such an effort must rest upon general background knowledge of the hospital as an institution, and the changes that it has brought about in medical care, as well as upon special knowledge of social processes and interpersonal relationships. Thus, before we attempt to probe, even in a preliminary way, the intricate social dynamics that become involved in any positive approach to more personal patient care, we shall attempt to single out for discussion some of the distinctive elements that complicate the patterns of hospital life.

It is helpful to recall, in the first place, that human beings throughout most of their history have confronted and dealt with disease primarily in a family and community context, in the midst of closely knit relationships of kith and kin, and by means of folkways for coping with illness that were interwoven with the general fabric of group life. In such a setting the same forces linked with the onset of a man's illness might be maneuvered to aid his recovery. The entire process could be envisaged by the therapist as an indigenous group experience over which, through his own familiarity with it, he could exert considerable influence. As a matter of course, the multiple and related aspects of the illness, physical and social, were comprehended and manipulated by the primitive medicine man, and later by the family physician, in a way which for the times proved to be remarkably effective. The therapist, of necessity, remained close to the family and community and dealt with them as operational units, often hitting upon ways to utilize constructively many personal and social variables within the general situation. However unscientific his approach, it was positive, personal, and relatively comprehensive. It has turned out that in historical perspective the achievements of this early therapist are highly commendable, especially in view of his lamentably poor knowledge of scientific medicine and his complete lack of social science knowledge.

Why do our contemporary physicians find it difficult to retain the notable assets of the family-physician role while making full use of the great modern scientific resources and institutionalized efficiencies and economies? This may be explained partly by the cleavage that has occurred and the gap that has widened between the home and the hospital. The physician does not know or deal so much with patients within the context of their accustomed life as did his predecessor; he must appraise and treat them on the basis of brief studies in his office, the clinic, or the hospital bed.

Some physicians have called attention to the gulf that separates the patient's manner of life at home from that in the hospital and the problem it creates both in diagnosis and therapy. Dr. John Paul points up this factor clearly with respect to the clinical teaching of medical students as applied to research in preventive medicine:

> These sick people are isolated "specimens." They are segregated from their environment, removed from the circumstances under which they became ill, separated from their families, stripped even of their clothes; all of which is done to create a proper atmosphere for diagnostic study and careful management on the physician's part, free from outside distractions. It may be trite to point out that these "outside distractions" are the very things which the modern doctor, or the student interested in preventive medicine, needs to study also. For if one is to handle patients adequately, it is necessary to bring clinical judgment to bear not only on the patient, but also on the circumstances under which his illness arose.[1]

The answer to this problem of the modern physician seems further to hinge on the nature of the institutional setting where he treats his patients. He finds it necessary to pursue his practice within surroundings that contrast sharply with those of his celebrated predecessor. Although his patients still acquire, incubate, and perhaps "cultivate" certain of their illnesses in family and community settings, he treats them in the hospital, as a member of a medical team, and in a more or less standardized service. He must administer to their needs amid what are for them strange and mysterious surroundings, and within an atmosphere of sharply professional and often very formal relationships. His patients are classified according to their illnesses, fitted into a tightly organized and scheduled system of hospital practices, and pressed into lines of conformity that are new and disturbing. They are, in short, forced with dispatch into a new role, that of the hospital patient, which makes specific and routine demands upon them. Then in their emergencies, they are cut off measurably from the tried and trusted contacts and supports of family and community. Indeed, in the patient's darkest hours, physically, mentally, and emotionally, he is likely to feel, and perhaps also to be left, rather much alone, especially if these periods

[1] Paul, J. R., "Preventive Medicine at Yale University School of Medicine, 1940–1949," *Yale Journal of Biology and Medicine*, vol. 22, January, 1950, p. 199.

come at night. In short, a doctor's patients are transplanted in a relatively helpless state into what constitutes for them something resembling an alien society and a divergent culture, where the problems of personal adaptation to emergencies can easily become magnified.

The physician, as well as other members of the hospital, finds himself, also, fitted by the system into a tight and pressing schedule in which he must somehow cope with these additional stresses that impinge upon his patients along with their illnesses. Thus, many problems inherent in modern patient care can be explained substantially by the fact that there has arisen in our highly institutionalized and measurably "ingrown" hospital system a significantly divergent culture, or subculture, with its own peculiar characteristics.

There is no question that for our times the walls of a modern medical center represent a sharp division between what we may call two divergent subcultures which meet and clash in the lives of those who experience or cope with sickness. The impact of this contrast can be felt by any socially perceptive person who crosses the threshold of an imposing hospital or who stands by to observe its effect on others as they enter, especially those coming for the first time to seek medical aid for themselves or for someone near and dear to them. Watching and listening on the side, it is easy to sense that the door of the hospital stands for the public as a symbol of entrance into a different and somewhat awesome world. Those who cross the threshold not infrequently manifest signs of anxiety and alarm, as is most obvious in the case of the patient himself.

The observer can, indeed, often sense a feeling of great relief on the part of the relatives that at last the patient is over the threshold and "from here on the nurses and medics are responsible." Perhaps, after all, in a social as well as a legal sense the most crucial feature of the hospital threshold is the sharp division in responsibility it represents. Thus, one may see a nurse or orderly transport a patient in a wheelchair to the hospital door, from which he walks away under his own power and often with noticeable vigor. The dividing line between two contrasting environments, and two separate jurisdictions, is frequently dramatized.

These social and cultural contrasts, which create in a sense two different "worlds," are further underlined by the fact that not only do those who have lived long *outside* the hospital fear to move *inside*, but some persons who have spent considerable time in this environment show signs of anxiety at the thought of leaving it. It is familiar knowledge to hospital personnel that when discharge is pending some of the "hospital-wise" and "ward-adapted" patients revive their old ailments or conjure up new ones. It is also true that some employees and professional staff members seem to identify so strongly with the hospital way of life and become so thoroughly accommodated to it that they hesitate to "go out into the world on their own." Thus, senior interns may be heard voicing anxiety as to whether, on the termination of their hospital assignments, they will be able to "make out well on the outside." The facts of this contrast between home and hospital are also evidenced by patients recently discharged from treatment who relate to friends on the outside "what happened," somewhat like travelers returning from distant places. One may also observe interns listening eagerly to physicians who return and tell what it is like "out in general practice." It is, thus, not difficult for one trained for sensitivity to such phenomena to become sharply aware in a general way of the divergent subcultural milieus in which sickness is faced, the home and the hospital.

It is no doubt the patient who generally feels the impact of the contrasts between home and hospital most deeply, for he undergoes the transition at a time when he is often weak and helpless, with stress potentials high and his adaptive resources low. Sharp changes in both the physical and the social environment may bear on him with special force. While at home the physical surroundings have been familiar and afforded a sense of security, the patient finds hospital surroundings strange and often disquieting. Added to this is the impression a patient can easily, and often justifiably, acquire, that something very serious is pending to require so detailed an examination, including the numerous tests which he must undergo. Indeed, the contrast between the environment of the home and of the hospital may be regarded by the physician as sufficiently upsetting in itself to justify certain prescribed sedations for a time in order to numb the patient's sensitivities to surrounding disturbances.

Further, if the patient is keenly aware of what is going on, it may become a major undertaking for him to try to participate in the culture of the hospital society, to conform acceptably, to play his "patient role" with success, and to put himself in line for securing the full benefits of the hospital service, including, of course, personal acceptance and reinforcements, rather than rejection and frustrations. Like any "outsider" seeking acceptance and security from an "ingroup," he faces a probationary period, possible misunderstandings, unexpected pitfalls, and perhaps some penalties. There is plenty of evidence that many patients go through a period of being "frightened and defensive" until they have achieved some working adjustment to their new situation.

Members of the hospital who are total strangers to the patient, and who may not even introduce themselves, begin to rule his life as to many minor details as well as in major matters. There are patients who have counted more than thirty different persons in the room during one day, each carrying varying degrees of authority. Some of these not infrequently appear to hold his life, if not his death, in their hands. The resident intern can come to appear to the patient all-powerful, and the nurse who is "in charge" exercises powers that may seem almost as vital. Even aids and orderlies find themselves in a position to grant or withhold what are actually small favors but which come to be very important. One patient, after a period of hospitalization in a highly rated institution where he received excellent technical care, declared emphatically: "I was glad to get out; a hospital is no place for a sick man. When you are in a hospital you should be able to *defend* yourself."[1]

The sense of apprehension fostered by these various conditions within the hospital is strengthened by the patient's loss of prerogatives. In our western tradition, a man's home is still his fortress, if not his castle, and even though he becomes a patient there he still retains a proprietary sense for his rights and privileges, and he can insist that he be treated measurably in accordance with these claims. In addition, he is generally reinforced in his position by friends and by family sentiments that accord to him special concessions because of his sickness.

In contrast, the sick man's personal prerogatives, in the usual case,[2] undergo very important changes when he is moved out of *his* home and *his own* bed into the hospital and one of *its* beds. Whereas at home he retained his work-a-day apparel and accoutrements which helped to fortify his sense of competence and self-reliance, in the hospital all of these, and the associated symbols of power and individuality, are stripped from him and locked away out of sight or even sent back to his home. He is left with his naked, and perhaps not very impressive, self and with only a standard hospital jacket for a cover.

Symbols of the sense of dependence and apprehension the patient may feel in the hospital, in contrast to his feeling of independence and security in the home, are easy to spot in prevailing practice and in the conventional terminology employed. In the hospital, for instance, the patient rings the bell

[1] Personal communication from Dr. D. W. Roberts.

[2] It should be granted that the patient who has been less favorably situated at home may find the disadvantages of hospital life less obvious. Those who have fewer prerogatives at home suffer less from the change of role, or may even find their situation improved in the hospital. Indeed, it is not unusual to hear an underprivileged person declare during his stay, "I have never had it so good before in my life."

and waits prayerfully for nurse or doctor, while at home the nurse or doctor rings the bell and waits to be let in. In the hospital the patient is "admitted" and "discharged" and all the relatives are visitors under rules, while at home the physician is "on call" and can be "changed," and the nurse is "hired" and can be "fired." In the home "prescriptions" are requested and filled out, but in the hospital "orders" are written and must be enforced. In the hospital patients are moved from place to place often without any explanation, whereas at home they are likely to be "led about" with more personal consideration and persuasion. In the home medical advisers and nurses come, and they may go, while the patient stays on; but in the hospital the tenure is in the reverse, and this can be a decided disadvantage for the patient's prerogatives. While some patients doubtless find greater social, as well as physical security in the hospital than in their homes, the majority seem to feel the need to steel themselves especially for the change.

Special note should be made of the fact that illness is often complicated, if not caused, by conflict in the family and community and that the fears and confusion of the hospital may appear to the patient less severe and more tolerable than those experienced at home. In such a case the hospital patient may be compared to the transcultural migrant who, in preference to coping with stresses at the home base, elects to escape from old conditions even though major changes and adjustments are involved. In fact, a solution by escape rarely proves satisfactory, since the stress-evoking situations can be so easily duplicated or generalized and may again elicit the previously conditioned protective reaction patterns. Or, on the other hand, even when symptoms disappear after admission to the hospital, they may recur when the patient returns to his former situation. Then, no constructive therapy has taken place, and the hospital may be said to have served only as a temporary asylum or retreat. An essential issue in therapy is to bridge the gap between home and hospital in ways that assist and forward the rehabilitation of the patient. This requires comprehension of a patient's social background as well as tools that are suitable for dealing with that background.

Furthermore, while the patient was at home, he was obviously the sickest person in the family circle, and thus deserving of special attention and consideration because of his predicament and also because of the kind of person he was remembered as being when in good health. In the hospital, and especially if on a ward, he is "just another patient" who cannot rely on the staff's knowledge of his usual capacities and personal charms to qualify his present plight. Moreover, there are other patients all around him who appear to be more seriously ill than he, and they may seem to require, and perhaps get, much more consideration than he does. Indeed, a very common pitfall for the entering patient is that he anticipates more attention than he is likely to receive, a misinterpretation which may be due solely to his lack of sophistication concerning the contrasting realities of home and hospital life.

Learning to play his new role in the hospital may in itself prove an arduous task. Stresses in this area may be accentuated for the patient by the not infrequent reminder that if his behavior fails to meet approval, he may be labeled "uncooperative" and be treated accordingly. This can easily constitute a threat and prompt a sensitive and conforming person to act even when very ill, as though the burden of smooth relationships in the hospital, and perhaps the success of his treatment, rested largely upon himself. In this case he may try to become a "model patient," and be unduly self-denying and apologetic about even the necessary demands he makes upon the staff. The free and frequent way in which the label "uncooperative patient" gets bandied about in our hospitals is perhaps symbolic of the misunderstandings and personal accusations that generally occur when individuals are brought together from contrasting subcultural backgrounds. There is no question that its usage promotes untold damage in interpersonal relationships and often at times when the patients are undergoing crises in their illnesses.[1]

Thus, in many situations and diverse circumstances one may observe the patient coping with other anxieties than those caused by his illness as he learns to play his new role acceptably and strives to find his place in the sharply stratified social system of the hospital. And, more often than not, the place of the patient in this complex structure, as one physician dryly remarked, is "at the bottom of the totem pole."

At this point, as we are viewing the patient in the process of working out adaptations to his new hospital environment, it will be helpful to recall the four typical patterns which individuals follow in relating themselves to society and its culture.[2]

As a culture-creature the individual is somewhat passive and submissive to the forces around him. In a hospital setting this pattern of acceptance and compliance seems generally encouraged, if not positively inculcated. A classic and probably extreme example of the creature-type of adaptation is the patient who reported that he said to the surgeon just before undergoing a major operation: "Doctor, I am now completely in your hands. I'll sign any paper or do whatever I am told. Whatever you do will be O.K. And if I don't come out of this, that will be O.K., too." The patient said later that he was praised highly in the hospital for "such a wonderful attitude."

And there is the example of the old man of eighty, with a record of excessive internal bleeding, and many transfusions, who on his third admission to the hospital commented to the nurse: "You know this is really a wonderful place. Twice I have come in here expecting to die, and twice I have walked out alive. Some day I will come in and die, and then I'll be glad it happened here."

[1] See Schwartz, A. B., "The Relationship of Home and Hospital in the Management of Sick Children," 1934; Stevenson, G. S., editor, *Administrative Medicine*, 1953.

[2] See pp. 77–79.

It is probably impossible, without considerable study, to draw a fine dividing line between the points in a patient's responses where trustful and submissive behavior proves to be an asset to recovery and rehabilitation on the one hand or a liability on the other. An extreme pose of confidence and compliance, when events take a turn for the worse, may give way to the opposite attitudes, and with corresponding extremes of distrust and opposition to treatment. Compliance, even in a hospital, when carried too far, can thus become a handicapping adaptation.

The carrier of culture, on the other hand, is more active with regard to the norms and codes of his groups, finding satisfaction in his exemplary conduct and the recognition for it that he strives to obtain. Perhaps he is best described as a responsible adult.

In hospital settings, for example, it is impressive to witness how desperately some persons will strive and suffer to fulfill the prevailing standards of a "model patient." Sometimes even staff members may all but forget the suffering, or overlook its futility, in admiration of the heroics. One proud, elderly woman, apparently symbolizing her culture's ideal of grit and courage in the face of stress, announced to the nurses upon her admission: "Let's be frank with each other while I am here. I want you to know that I am aware of the fact that I have cancer. I also want you to know that I am made of good stuff, and that there is going to be a stiff fight. I have been here before, and I am going to come in and go out several times more before I die."

Or, in a quieter vein, there was the teacher in her mid-thirties who had been admitted for general examinations and tests. She was informed by an intern at about 9:30 one night that she had cancer and probably could not live more than a few weeks. At 3:30 in the morning she was found by the floor nurse awake and restless, although she had signaled for no one. When questioned sympathetically, she divulged her ominous new knowledge and said quietly but with tears, "I have prayed all night for courage to carry me through." In a conference later, an experienced staff member commented praisefully, "She does not want to make a spectacle of herself."

There is no question that the culture-bearing, exemplary patient in the hospital, or person in society, who struggles inwardly and displays outwardly such poise in order to maintain a standard, constitutes a challenge for systematic study in situational context. He or she may be paying an excessive price as a carrier of the culture, a toll in stress that can be easily overlooked by all and perhaps ignored in therapy.

The third type of relationship between the individual and his culture is that of the creator. Potentially, at least, all individuals are capable of initiating change, but in hospital surroundings, where the pressure is for conformity and routine, innovations by the patient are rarely encouraged. Indeed, patients are regarded and treated more as irresponsible children than as adults. Sometimes, however, patients do create or devise original and effective ways of dealing with their problems in the hospital or they become potential resources for help and healing in their relationships with other patients. With new gains in longevity and increases in the so-called chronic diseases, there may be added incentive for patients to pioneer in the creation of new adaptations to prolonged sickness and debility.[1]

Finally, there is the individual who manipulates his culture, bending it for his own goals and uses. This relationship of a patient to his family or to the hospital is well known to clinicians. It is not unusual for an adroit or ingenious patient to maneuver himself into advantageous positions for securing the full benefits of staff and facilities, for gaining priority over other patients in medical and nursing care, and for keeping the staff (or his family) constantly on their toes. He may marshal

[1] See Simmons, L. W., "Social Participation of the Aged in Different Cultures," 1952.

and interpret codes of medical and nursing procedures to strengthen his claims and sometimes all but coerce staff members into prompt fulfillment of his whims, as well as his legitimate needs. Indeed, he may be able even to inspire sicker patients to sympathize with and make sacrifices for him. A person who is a gifted and somewhat inconsiderate manipulator of the norms, rules, and customs of the hospital can exercise not a few prerogatives from a sickbed. As a matter of fact, it may be possible for him to find himself more effective and better satisfied in illness than in health and settle down thereby in this state.

Even a sketchy knowledge of the chief roles that a patient may assume in relation to his over-all cultural standards and to the hospital society may go far to explain the motivations that underlie the behavior of individual patients under therapy. We soon come to view the patient not only as a person coping with physical pains and handicaps, but also as a social being who is sensitive to the responses and verdicts of his fellow agents in society, and who struggles to maintain in their eyes a position of one sort or another. Further, we may discover that the stresses and strains thus exerted upon him are multiplied and intensified within the complex hospital setting.

Stress Potentials in Hospital Practice

Modern medicine is able to rally to the patient's aid a vast array of new knowledge and technical procedures. It can sustain the breath of life under increasingly severe circumstances, especially in a great hospital with all its facilities. These remarkable accomplishments with human bodies, however, serve further to accentuate how far medical achievements based on treatment of the patient as an organism have advanced beyond those based upon knowledge of him as a person or personality.

At present, except in special departments or particular cases, the attention customarily paid by staff members to manifestations of the patient's physical disorders is in striking contrast to that paid to signs of mental or emotional disturbances. While the former are subject to routine inspection with immediate and precise remedial measures, the latter, as we have seen, are frequently overlooked until they become critical nursing problems or reach stages where risks to life or limb become evident, as for example in suicidal symptoms. Yet, as we now know, these two aspects of medical care cannot be divorced or viewed independently without jeopardizing the patient's welfare, for difficulties in one area are usually reflected in the other. Thus, frequently, patients are partially cured by expert physical skills while at the same time, paradoxically, their recovery is blocked by preventable or treatable personal stresses, some of which may actually arise within or become magnified by their hospital experiences. They may, indeed, suffer prolonged states of invalidism and "hospitalism," perhaps in a kind of vicious circle, as a result of their unresolved mental and emotional conflicts. New knowledge of the ways in which personal stress handicaps recovery and aggravates or perpetuates particular diseases is bound to stimulate further concern for patients' anxieties and frustrations. Any new methods of preventing, resolving, or even relieving the stresses that exceed safe limits of toleration hold out promise of further gains, often fundamental, in health and human welfare. With the increasing volume of recognized functional disorders in patient ailments, it may be that greater immediate gains in medical care are obtainable on the personal than on the physical side of the individual's adaptations to his life situation.

Such an orientation to the problems of illness brings about a far-reaching reappraisal of the elements with which therapy is concerned. The preventable or treatable stresses associated with sickness emerge as important intervening variables in medical care. This new focus on stress grows in significance as our knowledge increases concerning emotional states as parts of particular reaction patterns and which, in turn, are followed by ill effects on certain organs or parts of the body, as portrayed in Chapter 5. Such knowledge makes it possible to understand how an illness may become more grave even in a hospital where the patient has come expressly to be cured, and in spite of the excellent technical care which he may receive on a strictly physical plane. Personal stresses may become, thus, major factors to reckon with in successful therapy. We begin to anticipate that, in addition to the medical specifics indicated for identifiable disease entities, such as insulin for diabetes, digitalis for certain cardiac symptoms, and surgery for stomach ulcers, corresponding social specifics or methods of protecting the patient against or helping him cope with the stresses in his life, both individual and general, may come to be included more or less routinely in any therapeutic program.

It is true, to be sure, that certain stresses experienced by patients are both understandable and unavoidable by the very nature of illness and the realities of medical treatment. The hospital is necessarily a stress-laden society, for, as in all situations where gravely ill persons are concerned, certain types of stress must be admitted and accepted. Many of the sick who come for treatment can never get well. Some linger on in suffering; others may die suddenly. Death represents an unknown variable, the stress-evoking effects of which are intensified by fears of certain hazards in the hospital system, such as precarious operative procedures and apprehensions lest slips and oversights may arise from the complex divisions of responsibility. Physical pain is another outstanding example of a largely unavoidable stress, although patients may seek the hospital for the relief of pain. Most people come to the hospital because of pain primarily, and they can anticipate having to put up with more of it as part of their treatment, even when the prognosis is good. If, on the other hand, their condition continues to grow worse rather than better, increasing pain is compounded by dread of the outcome, which may also undermine the patient's fortitude.

Though modern drugs alleviate much physical suffering, and even when it is granted that psychological, social, and cultural variables play a large part in what patients experience of pain, it must still be accepted in general as an unavoidable source of stress. Because of the physical realities of illness, therefore, stress-inducing factors cannot be eliminated entirely from the hospital setting.

It is also possible to distinguish other types of stress, which, though potentially remediable, must be classed as more or less unavoidable because of the social realities of our culture and of our hospital system. Thus, for example, prejudices that run rife in American society can hardly be excluded fully from the treatment situations within the hospital. Even if staff members could be free from the prejudices and superstitions based on race, ethnic background, and class or creed, the patients will bring their own beliefs and biases into the hospital setting and, in giving expression to them, add personal stress to their other ailments and to the discomforts that their fellows must endure. In certain instances patients belonging to groups that are subject to prejudice in our society bring with them to the hospital such an acute sensitivity to slights of any kind that they constantly misinterpret common events as signs of discrimination. Thus, they judge as proof of prejudice the particular bed to which they are assigned, the liquid diet which is prescribed for them, or the withdrawal from them for another's use of a piece of apparatus that they no longer need. Although explicit explanations may help, it is often impossible to prevent such patients from making disturbing misinterpretations. In this way social realities of manifold types complicate and handicap smooth and supportive interpersonal relationships in institutionalized therapy. Because they are deeply rooted in our general culture, changes that might help to alleviate them are achieved very slowly indeed.

When we recognize that many of the stresses confronted in the hospital are unavoidable as products of our general culture or as a consequence of our hospital society and its contrasting culture, it then becomes important to ask whether there are other stresses that are avoidable or can be alleviated. With greater knowledge of the hospital system and the experience of patients, would it be possible to anticipate and relieve considerable amounts of stress, as for example, by a reorganization of certain services, alteration of prevalent and handicapping staff attitudes, or the use of new approaches and techniques in patient care? With this thought in mind, a preliminary effort was made to survey certain gross and over-all forms of patient frustration which might be substantially avoided or corrected. While no claim can be made for a comprehensive coverage of these problems, it may be helpful to list a few of the broad types of frequently encountered stresses which, according to our records, appear to be largely preventable or subject to improvement.

Perhaps foremost is the problem of patient orientation, which has already received considerable attention and some experimentation by hospital staffs. It would be difficult to overemphasize the fact that patients suffer great anxiety consequent to facing, in their helpless stages, a strange, mysterious, and awe-inspiring environment, which represents for them an "alien" culture. Since this remains a very common pitfall, the many unknowns of the new setting deserve careful explanation, not only in the first days of the patient's stay, but at every stage of his hospital experience. Again and again investigation of individual cases has shown that the worst days and nights of mental anguish could easily have been cleared up or greatly alleviated by a few simple explanations.

At this point, we anticipate a typical hospital attitude with respect to patients and what may be regarded as proper conduct on their part. After all, if they have confidence in their doctors, and if they can trust the nurse to know what the physicians believe to be best for them and to be capable of carrying out the prescribed orders, then why should they be asking many questions and slowing down the works? In short, the ideal for the cooperative patient is to accept his plight stoically, relax fully, trust the staff completely, and yield himself cheerfully into the hands of the hospital personnel. Constant questions can be interpreted as lack of confidence. Thus, tactful patients may learn to go sparingly on requests for explanations.

There is also a noticeable tendency on the part of some nursing staffs to set up water-tight compartments between what they regard as normal and abnormal responses and to judge more sternly those patients who are considered to exhibit the latter type of reaction. Two phrases are frequently encountered on the lips of staff members, and also in hospital case records. The patient "shows overly great bodily concern" or he "overly reacts to pain." To one not thoroughly steeped in the hospital culture, the use of these phrases is often startling because of the assumptions made as to patient equilibrium.

In addition to the normal-abnormal dichotomy with respect to patients' suffering, there is another sharp and rigid black-or-white line which is often drawn, with similar unfortunate effects upon staff attitudes. In the general service there is a tendency on the part of some staff members to jump to the conclusion that a patient is a "faker" or a "malingerer" whenever test evidence proves the presence of strong and disturbing emotional factors that becloud the physical elements of his illness. Thus, while the use of the sterile hypo or other placebos is perhaps justified in many cases as a harmless tension-relieving procedure, if the hypo does what it is supposed to do—gives relief—the patient concerned is likely to be subject to prejudice, and even some neglect or rejection. Again, there does not seem to be adequate understanding of the wide range of individual differences in reaction to be expected in any particular situation, nor of the fact that the presence of emotional factors does not prove that there is not also a general organic basis for the illness. This becomes all the more important since the very patient who manifests emotional symptoms is the one who may need the most careful attention.

Thus, it appears that like any other organized and deeply entrenched institution, our hospitals carry within their systems, and especially for the responsible staff member, certain vested interests, commitments, and predispositions for sensitivity and objectivity that are well developed and disciplined in particular areas of activity and less so in others. No disparagement is implied in the recognition of the social realities that exist, as far as we know, in all such tightly structured subdivisions of human society. Our purpose is to call attention to them for more systematic study and to explore some of their effects upon our present patient care and our potential medical security. It is thus hoped that participant observers from the outside, and otherwise oriented, may be able to discern data, identify processes, and formulate some of the dynamics that have been more or less overlooked or underemphasized by those who have become so intimate a part and product of the system.

CHAPTER 7

The Problems Reviewed

To TRAINED OBSERVERS in both fields it has long been apparent that medicine and social science are equally concerned, in their special ways, with human behavior. Medicine has devoted itself mainly to the study and treatment of that aspect of behavior which involves pain, illness, inappropriate physiological and organic responses; those phenomena, in short, that threaten the survival or comfort of the individual. Social science, on the other hand, has been preoccupied with the study of man in his social environment, the way in which social relationships are organized and carried on, the interactions of persons with different statuses and roles, and the relationship of all these to individual or social survival. There is, moreover, mutual interest in inappropriate social behavior or social pathology. Both medicine and social science have, in effect, selected certain aspects of mankind for their proper study and have developed appropriate concepts and methods for their particular concerns.

Recently, however, it has become more and more apparent that while each discipline has developed a "hard core" of central interests, peculiar to itself, each also makes some contact with the other. Social factors, such as customs and shared beliefs, that bring on or influence epidemics are clearly of concern to medicine; and, contrariwise, the hospital, which epitomizes modern medical research and practice, from a social science viewpoint is just another social institution involving a hierarchy of personnel, norms of procedure, and material equipment that may manifest lags and ineptitudes in adjustment. Of special significance for our purpose is the realization that personal and social factors can affect the onset of many common varieties of illness and disease, as well as the course and outcome of treatment.

In these circumstances a primary question from the standpoint of scientific progress is: how can research best be conducted? Should medical experts and social scientists go their separate ways, or should more active cooperation be sought? Clearly, the latter solution is more desirable, both for practical and for theoretical reasons.

It is evident that trained physicians and clinical specialists cannot become competent social scientists any more than professional social scientists can become expert physicians or clinicians. To be sure, either can pick up a "smattering of ignorance" concerning the problems, concepts, and methods of the other, but such fragmentary information gives little promise of leading to that degree of skill and knowledge that will advance sociomedical research. Thus, to the extent that their separate problems lead them into the areas of special knowledge contained by the other, collaboration is desirable. On the theoretical level as well, there is need for alliance and cooperation, inasmuch as the physical, personal, social, and cultural aspects of human life always come to a focus, in health or in illness, in a single individual. He is the vortex of these various forces, the center of interaction among them.

Granting, then, the necessity and desirability of increased partnership between medicine and social science, how can this best be accomplished? It would seem that certain prerequisites must be met before we can anticipate many results from an active sociomedical alliance. In the first place, it is still necessary to alert some of the personnel of both disciplines as to their areas of common concern. Second, the most relevant concepts of both sides must be made accessible, understandable, and meaningful to interested persons in both fields of endeavor. And, finally, some tentative conceptual links, pointing to problems and possible modes of solution, must be made between the biophysical orientation of medicine and the sociocultural orientation of social science.

This book is an attempt to meet the conditions named. Throughout there runs the theme of alerting physicians, nurses, and clinicians to those aspects of a patient's environment that affect his illness and its prognosis. Without disparaging the central medical focus on biophysical phenomena, we call the attention of medical and hospital personnel to phases of human relationships that may be interfering with their routines and with their expected results. At the same time, certain clues are offered for the analysis and interpretation of personal-social factors in medical context.

Similarly, an attempt has been made here to clarify and elaborate those central concepts of social science that bear most directly upon medical problems. The basic notion of the individual as simultaneously behaving as a physical organism, an agent-member of society, and a personality in a given cultural context may be useful in supplying a much-needed focus on the patient, or potential patient, as an individual resembling many others, but also with certain unique features. The other concepts, like society, culture, subgroups and subcultures, habituated attitudes, the "situation," and the "definition of the situation," similarly provide conceptual tools useful alike to the practitioner or the investigator.

And, finally, we suggest in summary certain tentative formulations of the psychological and social dynamics relating to illness and its treatment:

1. Socially derived stresses that evoke inept protective reaction patterns on the part of the patient not infrequently result in disease and its complications.

2. A patient's previously conditioned and stress-laden social situation, which has become linked with his inept reaction patterns, has a special power to exacerbate his illness and retard treatment.

3. There may arise, also, within the hospital situation what may be called general stress-evoking elements, which further complicate illness and retard recovery for the patient, especially when these elements become related to, or generalized from, his previously established stress-reaction patterns.

4. Any knowledge of either the special and long-established, or recent and generalized stress-evolving situations in the life of the patient, which become linked to his inept reaction patterns, provides the therapist with additional leverage for control of the patient's responses and the course of the disease.

5. A lack of knowledge of the special or general stress-evoking situations in the life of the patient leaves the therapist liable to the danger of inadvertently introducing or tolerating within the treatment situation the very stress-charged elements that activate the harmful protective reaction patterns and exacerbate the illness, or sometimes push the patient further into invalidism.

Each patient may be thus viewed in the network of his human relationships, and in terms of the relative amount of stress or support he received from them. Is the illness, the patient's attitude toward the illness, or his optimism or pessimism regarding its outcome related to his family relationships, difficulties on the job, or in other areas of living such as religion or economic insecurity? Are the personal stresses further complicated, inadvertently, by the institutionalized treatment situation? What positive factors and behavior in the patient's life situation evoke the reaction patterns conducive to health? What techniques are necessary to elucidate these and how can they be supplied? Can these related aspects of the social environment be controlled or modified so as to influence favorably the course of therapy and perhaps also the patient's general outlook?

At present, answers to such questions are necessarily vague and inconclusive. Moreover, from the standpoint of scientific goals, they must be sought in each individual case by exhaustive life histories and other techniques necessary to amass the relevant data bearing on the single person. But with the perspectives as we have attempted to outline them in this book it may be possible so to direct sociomedical research as to lead to the discovery of verifiable relationships that will henceforth ease the therapeutic burden by virtue of the greater prediction and control that the new knowledge will lend.

It should be emphasized, however, that sociomedical collaboration should not be regarded as a new magic talisman that will provide all the necessary answers. In terms of research, the process must be regarded as an endless one, each new solution giving rise to further problems which in turn will be subjected to further refinement and further study. Moreover, since the social environment, and an individual's relation to it, is constantly in a process of change, the generalizations applicable at one point in time may not last long, thus creating new research demands and further opportunities for verification.

And on the side of therapy, the caution must likewise be made that the sociomedical alliance, no matter how fruitful, will not provide easy generalizations that will lead to mechanical application in this case as well as the next. It may well be that in given instances, even though the social and psychological dynamics of the illness are known, as to the recommended course of treatment, the knowledge itself may not be sufficient to solve the physician's problem. It is entirely possible that a plan of treatment for a particular person will run into conflict with other spheres of recognized responsibility. Whenever, for example, elements appear in an illness that are the result of personal adaptations to stress in social situations, the elimination of the need of these protective reaction patterns on the part of the patient may upset long-standing relationships in his life and ill fit him for his accustomed role in society. Thus, if a person's illness is related to extreme dependency on his part to another, or if it is related to marital problems, or the like, its resolution may well mean disruption of a family, divorce, or other consequences that conflict with deep values in our culture.

Of course, this caution is not new in medicine, for it frequently happens that a drug or a treatment cannot be given a patient because other physical conditions make it dangerous to do so. Thus, perhaps, we can recognize anew the fact that the medical art cannot be practiced in a detached, unindividualized manner. Even when the physician possesses the relevant knowledge for treatment and cures, he will also consider a wide variety of factors that bear upon the condition of the particular patient. In these circumstances his professional responsibility is not so clearly defined and he will make decisions in terms of his own ethical and moral evaluations.

Thus, it may be that a particular individual is "better off" *with* his illness, or that he or his associates are ill prepared to pay the price of full recovery. Such are the complexities and the problems of equilibrium in personal and social relationships. Indeed, the very best that all the sciences are able to contribute to the medical profession will probably still leave much to be desired in terms of comprehensive therapy. But for medicine to neglect what can be learned from any source would clearly be out of harmony with its history and purpose as a profession dedicated to the alleviation of human suffering. And, likewise, should social scientists fail to respond to these new developments in medicine, they would be missing a rare opportunity to gather invaluable data and to test their theories in what approximates for them a social "laboratory" of great importance.

Bibliography

ABERLE, DAVID F., "The Psychosocial Analysis of a Hopi Life-History," *Comparative Psychology Monographs*, vol. 21, December, 1951. 133 pp.

ACKERKNECHT, ERWIN H., "Natural Diseases and Rational Treatment in Primitive Medicine," *Bulletin of the History of Medicine*, vol. 19, May, 1946, pp. 467–497.

"On the Collecting of Data Concerning Primitive Medicine," *American Anthropologist*, vol. 47, July, 1945, pp. 427–432.

"Primitive Medicine and Culture Pattern," *Bulletin of the History of Medicine*, vol. 12, November, 1942, pp. 545–574.

"Primitive Surgery," *American Anthropologist*, vol. 49, January, 1947, pp. 25–45.

"Problems of Primitive Medicine," *Bulletin of the History of Medicine*, vol. 11, May, 1942, pp. 503–521.

"Psychopathology, Primitive Medicine, and Primitive Culture," *Bulletin of the History of Medicine*, vol. 14, June, 1943, pp. 30–67.

ACKERMAN, NATHAN W., "'Social Role' and Total Personality," *American Journal of Orthopsychiatry*, vol. 21, January, 1951, pp. 1–17.

ADORNO, T. W., AND OTHERS, *The Authoritarian Personality*. Harper and Bros., New York, 1950. 990 pp.

ALEXANDER, FRANZ, *Psychosomatic Medicine:* Its Principles and Application. W. W. Norton and Co., New York, 1950. 300 pp.

ALLEE, WARDER C., *Cooperation Among Animals*, with Human Implications. Henry Schuman, Inc., New York, 1951. 233 pp.

The Social Life of Animals. W. W. Norton and Co., New York, 1938. 293 pp.

ALLEN, RAYMOND B., *Medical Education and the Changing Order*. Commonwealth Fund, New York, 1946. 142 pp.

Medicine in the Changing Order. Studies of the New York Academy of Medicine. Commonwealth Fund, New York, 1947. 240 pp.

ALLPORT, GORDON W., "Attitudes" in *A Handbook of Social Psychology*, edited by Carl A. Murchison, 1935, pp. 798–844.

The ABC's of Scapegoating. Antidefamation League, New York, 1948. 56 pp.

The Use of Personal Documents in Psychological Science. Social Science Research Council, Bulletin 49, New York, 1942. 210 pp.

ALLPORT, GORDON W., AND L. J. POSTMAN, *The Psychology of Rumor*. Henry Holt and Co., New York, 1947. 247 pp.

ALMY, T. P., AND OTHERS, "Constipation and Diarrhea as Reactions to Life Stress," *Proceedings* of the Association for Research in Nervous and Mental Disease, vol. 29, 1950, pp. 724–731.

ALSTED, GUNNAR, *Studies on the Changing Incidence of Peptic Ulcer of the Stomach and Duodenum*. Oxford University Press, London, 1939. 148 pp.

ANDERSON, ODIN W., "The Sociologist and Medicine: Generalizations from a Teaching and Research Experience in a Medical School," *Social Forces*, vol. 31, October, 1952, pp. 38–42.

ANDERSON, VICTOR V., *Psychiatry in Industry*. Harper and Bros., New York, 1929. 364 pp.

ANGYAL, ANDRÁS, *Foundations for a Science of Personality*. Commonwealth Fund, New York, 1941. 398 pp.

ASHFORD, MAHLON, editor, *Trends in Medical Education*. Commonwealth Fund, New York, 1949. 320 pp.

ASHLEY-MONTAGUE, FRANCIS, "The Sociobiology of Man," *Scientific Monthly*, vol. 50, June, 1940, pp. 483–490.

BABER, RAY E., *Marriage and the Family*. 2d ed. McGraw-Hill Book Co., New York, 1953. 719 pp.

BAEHR, GEORGE, "The Peckham Experiment," *Milbank Memorial Fund Quarterly*, vol. 22, October, 1944, pp. 352–357.

BAIN, READ, "Action Research and Group Dynamics," *Social Forces*, vol. 30, October, 1951, pp. 1–10.

"An Attitude on Attitude Research," *American Journal of Sociology*, vol. 33, May, 1928, pp. 940–957.

"Theory and Measurement of Attitudes and Opinions," *Psychological Bulletin*, vol. 27, May, 1930, pp. 357–379.

BAKER, ZELMA, J. F. FAZEKAS, AND HAROLD E. HIMWICH, "Carbohydrate Oxidation in Normal and Diabetic Cerebral Tissues," *Journal of Biological Chemistry*, vol. 125, October, 1938, pp. 545–556.

BALES, ROBERT F., *Interaction Process Analysis:* A Method for the Study of Small Groups. Addison-Wesley Press, Cambridge, Mass., 1950. 203 pp.

BARKER, ROGER G., AND OTHERS, *Adjustment to Physical Handicap and Illness:* A Survey of the Social Psychology of Physique and Disability. Social Science Research Council, Bulletin 55 rev., New York, 1953. 440 pp. See especially "The Somatophysical Problem," pp. 1–13; "Somatopsychological Aspects of Differences in Physical Size, Strength, and Attractiveness," pp. 14–58; and "Social Psychology of Acute Illness," pp. 309–345.

BARNETT, HOMER G., "Invention and Cultural Change," *American Anthropologist*, vol. 44, January, 1942, pp. 14–30.

BARNOUW, VICTOR, *Acculturation and Personality Among the Wisconsin Chippewa.* Memoirs of the American Anthropological Association, Menasha, Wis., 1950, no. 72. 152 pp.

BARR, DAVID P., "The Changing Order in Medicine," *The Diplomate*, vol. 22, January, 1950, pp. 27–30.

BATESON, GREGORY, "Cultural Determinants of Personality" in *Personality and the Behavior Disorders*, edited by J. McV. Hunt, vol. 2, 1944, pp. 714–735.

"Sex and Culture," *Annals* of the New York Academy of Sciences, vol. 47, May, 1947, pp. 647–660.

BAYNE-JONES, STANHOPE, "The Hospital as a Center of Preventive Medicine," *The Diplomate*, vol. 22, January, 1950, pp. 1–8.

BEAGLEHOLE, ERNEST, "Culture and Psychosis in New Zealand," *Journal of the Polynesian Society*, vol. 48, September, 1939, pp. 144–155.

BEALE, BEATRICE B., AND OTHERS, "A Clinical Guide to Prognosis in Stress Diseases," *Journal of the American Medical Association*, vol. 149, August 30, 1952, pp. 1624–1628.

BELL, JOHN E., *Projective Techniques:* A Dynamic Approach to the Study of the Personality. Longmans, Green and Co., New York, 1948. 533 pp.

BENDIX, REINHARD, AND S. M. LIPSET, editors, *Class, Status and Power*. The Free Press, Glencoe, Ill., 1953. 725 pp.

BENEDEK, THERESE, *Insight and Personality Adjustment:* A Study of the Psychological Effects of War. Ronald Press Co., New York, 1946. 307 pp.

BENEDICT, RUTH, "Anthropology and the Abnormal," *Journal of Psychology*, vol. 10, January, 1934, pp. 59–82.

"Continuities and Discontinuities in Cultural Conditioning," *Psychiatry*, vol. 1, May, 1938, pp. 161–167.

Patterns of Culture. Houghton Mifflin Co., Boston, 1934. 291 pp.

BENNETT, JOHN W., "Culture Change and Personality in a Rural Society," *Social Forces*, vol. 23, December, 1944, pp. 123–132.

BENNETT, JOHN W., AND M. M. TUMIN, *Social Life:* Structure and Function. Alfred A. Knopf, Inc., New York, 1949. 725 pp.

BERNARD, JESSIE S., *American Family Behavior*. Harper and Bros., New York, 1942. 564 pp.

BETTELHEIM, BRUNO, "Individual and Mass Behavior in Extreme Situations," *Journal of Abnormal and Social Psychology*, vol. 38, October, 1943, pp. 417–452.

BILLIG, OTTO, JOHN GILLIN, AND WILLIAM DAVIDSON, "Aspects of Personality and Culture in a Guatemalan Community: Ethnological and Rorschach Approaches," Parts I and II, *Journal of Personality*, vol. 16, September, 1947, pp. 153–187, March, 1948, pp. 326–368.

BINGER, CARL, *More About Psychiatry*. University of Chicago Press, 1949. 201 pp.

BLAKE, R. R., AND G. V. RAMSEY, editors, *Perception:* An Approach to Personality. Ronald Press Co., New York, 1951. 442 pp.

BLUMER, HERBERT, *An Appraisal of Thomas and Znaniecki's "The Polish Peasant in Europe and America."* Social Science Research Council, Bulletin 44, New York, 1939. 210 pp.

BOGARDUS, EMORY S., "Social Distance and Its Origins," *Journal of Applied Sociology*, vol. 9, January, 1925, pp. 216–226.

"Social Distance: A Measuring Stick," *Survey*, vol. 56, May 1, 1926, pp. 169–170.

BONNER, HUBERT, "Field Theory and Sociology," *Sociology and Social Research*, vol. 33, January, 1949, pp. 171–179.

Social Psychology: An Interdisciplinary Approach. American Book Co., New York, 1953. 439 pp. See especially "Attitudes and Behavior," pp. 172–200.

BORTZ, E. L., "Social Components in Medicine," *Annals of Internal Medicine*, vol. 14, December, 1940, pp. 1065–1074.

BOSSARD, JAMES H. S., *The Sociology of Child Development*. Harper and Bros., New York, 1948. 790 pp.

BRIFFAULT, ROBERT, *The Mothers*. Macmillan Co., New York, 1927. 3 vols.

BRIGGS, ARTHUR E., "Social Distance Between Lawyers and Doctors," *Sociology and Social Research*, vol. 13, November, 1928, pp. 156–163.

BROWN, G. GORDON, "Culture, Society and Personality: A Restatement," *American Journal of Psychiatry*, vol. 108, September, 1951, pp. 173–175.

BROWN, G. GORDON, AND J. H. BARNETT, "Social Organization and Social Structure," *American Anthropologist*, vol. 44, January, 1942, pp. 31–36.

BROWN, JUDSON S., AND I. E. FARBER, "Emotions Conceptualized as Intervening Variables, with Suggestions Toward a Theory of Frustration," *Psychological Bulletin*, vol. 48, November, 1951, pp. 465–495.

BROWN, JUNIUS F., *Psychology and the Social Order:* An Introduction to the Dynamic Study of Social Fields. McGraw-Hill Book Co., New York, 1936. 529 pp.

BRUNO, FRANK J., "The Situational Approach: A Reaction to Individualism," *Social Forces*, vol. 9, June, 1931, pp. 482–483.

Trends in Social Work. Columbia University Press, New York, 1948. 387 pp.

BRYSON, LYMAN, AND OTHERS, *Conflicts of Power in Modern Culture:* Seventh Symposium of the Conference on Science, Philosophy and Religion, 1946. Harper and Bros., New York, 1947. 703 pp.

Buell, Bradley, and others, *Community Planning for Human Services*. Columbia University Press, New York, 1952. 464 pp. See especially "The Strategic Characteristics of Disease," pp. 144–169; "Some Strategic Characteristics of Maladjustment," pp. 252–272.

Burgess, Ernest W., and H. J. Locke, *The Family:* From Institution to Companionship. 2d ed. American Book Co., New York, 1953. 743 pp.

Burgess, Ernest W., and Paul Wallin, *Engagement and Marriage*. J. B. Lippincott Co., Philadelphia, 1953. 819 pp.

Cannon, Ida M., *On the Social Frontier of Medicine:* Pioneering in Medical Social Service. Harvard University Press, Cambridge, 1952. 273 pp.

"Some Clinical Aspects of Social Medicine," *New England Journal of Medicine*, vol. 234, January 3, 1946, pp. 20–23.

Cannon, Walter B., *Bodily Changes in Pain, Hunger, Fear and Rage*. 2d ed. D. Appleton and Co., New York, 1929. 404 pp.

"The Role of Emotion in Disease," *Annals of Internal Medicine*, vol. 9, May, 1936, pp. 1453–1465.

The Wisdom of the Body. 2d ed. W. W. Norton and Co., New York, 1939. 333 pp.

"'Voodoo' Death," *American Anthropologist*, vol. 44, April, 1942, pp. 169–181.

Cantril, Hadley, *The Psychology of Social Movements*. John Wiley and Sons, New York, 1941. 274 pp.

Caplow, Theodore, and R. E. Forman, "Neighborhood Interaction in a Homogeneous Community," *American Sociological Review*, vol. 15, June, 1950, pp. 357–366.

Carlson, Earl R., *Born That Way*. John Day Co., New York, 1941. 174 pp.

Carpenter, C. R., "A Field Study of the Behavior and Social Relations of Howling Monkeys," *Comparative Psychology Monographs*, vol. 10, May, 1934. 168 pp.

"Characteristics of Social Behavior in Non-Human Primates," *Transactions* of the New York Academy of Sciences, Series II, vol. 4, April, 1942, pp. 256–257.

CARR, LOWELL J., "Situational Sociology," *American Journal of Sociology*, vol. 51, September, 1945, pp. 136–141.

CARTWRIGHT, DORWIN, AND J. R. P. FRENCH, JR., "The Reliability of Life-History Studies," *Character and Personality*, vol. 8, December, 1939, pp. 110–119.

CASSIRER, ERNST, *An Essay on Man:* An Introduction to a Philosophy of Human Culture. Yale University Press, New Haven, 1944. 237 pp.

CATTELL, RAYMOND B., *Description and Measurement of Personality.* World Book Co., Yonkers, N. Y., 1946. 602 pp.

CAUDILL, WILLIAM, "Applied Anthropology in Medicine" in *Anthropology Today*, edited by A. L. Kroeber, 1953, pp. 771–806.

CAUDILL, WILLIAM, AND BERTRAM H. ROBERTS, "Pitfalls in the Organization of Interdisciplinary Research," *Human Organization*, vol. 10, Winter, 1951, pp. 12–15.

CAUDILL, WILLIAM, AND OTHERS, "Social Structure and Interaction Processes on a Psychiatric Ward," *American Journal of Orthopsychiatry*, vol. 22, April, 1952, pp. 314–334.

CAVAN, RUTH S., *The American Family.* Thomas Y. Crowell Co., New York, 1953. 658 pp.

CENTERS, RICHARD, *The Psychology of Social Classes:* A Study of Class Consciousness. Princeton University Press, Princeton, 1949. 244 pp.

CHAPIN, F. STUART, *Experimental Designs in Sociological Research.* Harper and Bros., New York, 1947. 206 pp.

"Latent Culture Patterns of the Unseen World of Social Reality," *American Journal of Sociology*, vol. 40, July, 1934, pp. 61–68.

The Measurement of Social Status by the Use of the Social Status Scale. University of Minnesota Press, Minneapolis, 1933. 16 pp.

CHARLES, LUCILE H., "Drama in Shaman Exorcism," *Journal of American Folklore*, vol. 66, April, 1953, pp. 95–122.

CHASE, STUART, *The Proper Study of Mankind:* An Inquiry into the Science of Human Relations. Harper and Bros., New York, 1948. 311 pp.

CHILD, IRVIN L., *Italian or American?* The Second Generation in Conflict. Yale University Press, New Haven, 1943. 208 pp.

CHILDE, VERE G., *Social Evolution.* Henry Schuman, Inc., New York, 1952. 184 pp.

CLARK, DUNCAN W., "The Social Environment as a Concern of Preventive Medicine," *Conference of Professors of Preventive Medicine Newsletter*, vol. 2, June, 1951, pp. 2–3. Multigraphed.

CLARK, KATHARINE G., *Preventive Medicine in Medical Schools:* Report of Colorado Springs Conference. Waverly Press, Baltimore, 1953. 123 pp.

CLAUSEN, JOHN A., "Social Science Research in the National Mental Health Program," *American Sociological Review*, vol. 15, June, 1950, pp. 402–409.

CLEMENTS, FORREST E., "Primitive Concepts of Disease," *University of California Publications* in American Archaeology and Ethnology, vol. 32, 1932, pp. 185–252.

COBB, STANLEY, *Emotions and Clinical Medicine.* W. W. Norton and Co., New York, 1950. 243 pp. See especially "Patterns of Personality," pp. 183–196; "The Problem of Specificity in Psychosomatic Reactions," pp. 197–211.

COLWELL, ALEXANDER H., "Social and Environmental Factors in Medicine," *Journal of the Association of American Medical Colleges*, vol. 21, May, 1946, pp. 160–164.

COMMISSION ON HOSPITAL CARE, *Hospital Care in the United States.* Commonwealth Fund, New York, 1947. 631 pp.

COMMONWEALTH FUND, *Thirty-fourth Annual Report*, New York, 1952. 41 pp.

COMMUNITY SERVICE SOCIETY OF NEW YORK, *The Family in a Democratic Society:* Anniversary Papers. Columbia University Press, New York, 1949. 287 pp.

COOLEY, CHARLES H., *Human Nature and the Social Order.* Charles Scribner's Sons, New York, 1902. 460 pp.

CORLETT, WILLIAM T., *The Medicine-Man of the American Indian and His Cultural Background.* Charles C. Thomas, Springfield, Ill., 1935. 369 pp.

COTTRELL, LEONARD S., JR., "Some Neglected Problems in Social Psychology," *American Sociological Review*, vol. 15, December, 1950, pp. 705–712.

"The Adjustment of the Individual to His Age and Sex Roles," *American Sociological Review*, vol. 7, October, 1942, pp. 617–620.

"The Analysis of Situational Fields in Social Psychology," *American Sociological Review*, vol. 7, June, 1942, pp. 370–382.

"The Case-Study Method in Prediction," *Sociometry*, vol. 4, November, 1941, pp. 358–370.

COUTU, WALTER, *Emergent Human Nature:* A Symbolic Field Interpretation. Alfred A. Knopf, Inc., New York, 1949. 432 pp.

CRANDALL, L. A., JR., "A Comparison of Ketosis in Man and Dog," *Journal of Biological Chemistry*, vol. 138, March, 1941, pp. 123–128.

CREW, F. A. E., "Social Medicine: An Academic Discipline and an Instrument of Social Policy," *Lancet*, vol. 2, November 11, 1944, pp. 617–619.

CURRAN, JEAN A., AND ELEANOR COCKERILL, *Widening Horizons in Medical Education:* A Study of the Teaching of Social and Environmental Factors in Medicine. Report of the Joint Committee of the Association of American Medical Colleges and the American Association of Medical Social Workers. Commonwealth Fund, New York, 1948. 228 pp.

DAI, BINGHAM, "Personality Problems in Chinese Culture," *American Sociological Review*, vol. 6, October, 1941, pp. 688–696.

DARK, E. P., "Sociological Medicine: Its Meaning and Scope," *Medical Journal of Australia*, vol. 1, January 13, 1945, pp. 31–34.

DAVEY, L. M., AND OTHERS, "The Effects on Gastric Secretion of Frontal Lobe Stimulation," *Proceedings* of the Association for Research in Mental and Nervous Disease, vol. 29, 1950, pp. 617–627.

DAVIE, MAURICE R., *Refugees in America:* Report of the Committee for the Study of Recent Immigration from Europe. Harper and Bros., New York, 1947. 45 pp.

"The Patterns of Urban Growth" in *Studies in the Science of Society*, edited by George P. Murdock, 1937, pp. 133–163.

DAVIS, ALLISON, AND JOHN DOLLARD, *Children of Bondage:* The Personality Development of Negro Youth in the Urban South. American Council on Education, Washington, 1940. 299 pp.

DAVIS, ALLISON, AND ROBERT J. HAVIGHURST, *Father of the Man:* How Your Child Gets Its Personality. Houghton Mifflin Co., Boston, 1947. 245 pp.

DAVIS, KINGSLEY, *Human Society.* Macmillan Co., New York, 1949. 655 pp.

DAVIS, KINGSLEY, AND W. E. MOORE, "Some Principles of Stratification," *American Sociological Review*, vol. 10, April, 1945, pp. 242–249.

DENNIS, WAYNE, *The Hopi Child.* Appleton-Century Co., New York, 1940. 204 pp.

"The Socialization of the Hopi Child" in *Language, Culture, and Personality:* Essays in Memory of Edward Sapir, edited by Leslie Spier and others, 1941, pp. 259–271.

DEVEREUX, GEORGE, *Reality and Dream:* Psychotherapy of a Plains Indian. International Universities Press, New York, 1951. 438 pp. See especially "Areal Culture Pattern and Areal Basic Personality," pp. 25–49.

"Institutionalized Homosexuality of the Mohave Indians," *Human Biology*, vol. 9, December, 1937, pp. 498–527.

"Mohave Culture and Personality," *Character and Personality*, vol. 8, December, 1939, pp. 91–109.

"Primitive Psychiatry," Parts I and II, *Bulletin of the History of Medicine*, vols. 8 and 11, October, 1940, pp. 1194–1213, May, 1942, pp. 522–542.

"Psychiatry and Anthropology: Some Research Objectives," *Bulletin of the Menninger Clinic*, vol. 16, September, 1952, pp. 167–177.

"Social Structure and the Economy of Affective Bonds," *Psychoanalytic Review*, vol. 29, July, 1942, pp. 303–314.

"The Logical Foundations of Culture and Personality Studies," *Transactions* of the New York Academy of Sciences, Series II, vol. 7, March, 1945, pp. 110–130.

"The Social Structure of a Schizophrenia Ward and Its Therapeutic Fitness," *Journal of Clinical Psychopathology*, vol. 6, October, 1944, pp. 231–265.

"The Social Structure of the Hospital as a Factor in Total Therapy," *American Journal of Orthopsychiatry*, vol. 19, July, 1949, pp. 492–500.

DEVEREUX, GEORGE, AND FLORENCE R. WEINER, "The Occupational Status of Nurses," *American Sociological Review*, vol. 15, October, 1950, pp. 628–634.

DICHTER, ERNEST, *A Psychological Study of the Doctor-Patient Relationship.* Paper submitted to California Medical Association, Alameda County, May, 1950. 30 pp.

DODD, STUART C., *A Controlled Experiment on Rural Hygiene in Syria.* Oxford University Press, London, 1934. 336 pp.

DOLLARD, JOHN, *Criteria for the Life History*, with Analyses of Six Notable Documents. Yale University Press, New Haven, 1935. 288 pp.

"Culture, Society, Impulse and Socialization," *American Journal of Sociology*, vol. 45, July, 1939, pp. 50–63.

DOLLARD, JOHN, AND NEAL E. MILLER, *Personality and Psychotherapy:* An Analysis in Terms of Learning, Thinking, and Culture. McGraw-Hill Book Co., New York, 1950. 488 pp.

DROBA, DANIEL D., "The Nature of Attitude," *Journal of Social Psychology*, vol. 4, November, 1933, pp. 444–463.

DuBOIS, CORA A., "Attitudes Toward Food and Hunger in Alor" in *Language, Culture, and Personality:* Essays in Memory of Edward Sapir, edited by Leslie Spier and others, 1941, pp. 272–281.

The People of Alor: A Social-Psychological Study of an East Indian Island. University of Minnesota Press, Minneapolis, 1944. 654 pp.

DUMMER, ETHEL S., editor, *The Unconscious:* A Symposium. Alfred A. Knopf, Inc., New York, 1928. 260 pp.

DUNBAR, HELEN F., *Mind and Body:* Psychosomatic Medicine. Random House, New York, 1947. 263 pp.

Psychosomatic Diagnosis. Paul B. Hoeber, Inc., New York, 1943. 741 pp.

Synopsis of Psychosomatic Diagnosis and Treatment. C. V. Mosby Co., St. Louis, 1948. 501 pp.

DUNHAM, HARMAN W., "Social Psychiatry," *American Sociological Review*, vol. 13, April, 1948, pp. 183–197.

"Topical Summaries of Current Literature: Social Attitudes," *American Journal of Sociology*, vol. 46, November, 1940, pp. 344–375.

DYK, WALTER, editor, *Old Mexican, Navaho Indian:* A Navaho Autobiography. Publications in Anthropology, no. 8. Viking Fund, New York, 1947. 218 pp.

Son of Old Man Hat: A Navaho Autobiography. Harcourt, Brace and Co., New York, 1938. 378 pp.

EGGAN, FREDERICK R., *Social Organization of the Western Pueblos.* University of Chicago Press, 1950. 373 pp.

ELIOT, THOMAS D., "The Adjustive Behavior of Bereaved Families: A New Field for Research," *Social Forces*, vol. 8, June, 1930, pp. 543–549.

"The Bereaved Family," *Annals* of the American Academy of Political and Social Science, vol. 160, March, 1932, pp. 184–190.

ELKIN, ADOLPHUS P., *Aboriginal Men of High Degree.* Australasian Publishing Co., Sydney, 1946. 148 pp.

ELLIS, EDGAR S., *Ancient Anodynes:* Primitive Anaesthesia and Allied Conditions. Wm. Heinemann, Ltd., London, 1946. 187 pp.

EMERSON, ALFRED E., "Basic Comparisons of Human and Insect Societies," *Biological Symposia*, vol. 8, 1942, pp. 163–176.

ERIKSON, ERIK H., *Childhood and Society.* W. W. Norton and Co., New York, 1950. 397 pp.

EVANS-PRITCHARD, EDWARD E., *Social Anthropology.* The Free Press, Glencoe, Ill., 1951. 134 pp.

Witchcraft, Oracles, and Magic Among the Azande. Oxford University Press, New York, 1937. 558 pp.

FARIS, ELLSWORTH, "Attitudes and Behavior," *American Journal of Sociology*, vol. 34, September, 1928, pp. 271–281.

"The Concept of Social Attitudes," *Journal of Applied Sociology*, vol. 9, July, 1925, pp. 404–409.

FARIS, ROBERT E. L., *Social Disorganization.* Ronald Press Co., New York, 1948. 481 pp.

Social Psychology. Ronald Press Co., New York, 1952. 420 pp.

FERGUSON, E. A. *The Theory and Practice of Medicine Among Preliterate Peoples.* Yale University, New Haven, 1947. Unpublished dissertation.

FERGUSON, LEONARD W., *Personality Measurement*. McGraw-Hill Book Co., New York, 1952. 457 pp.

"Primary Social Attitudes," *Journal of Psychology*, vol. 8, October, 1939, pp. 217–223.

FIELD, MARGARET J., *Religion and Medicine of the Gã People*. Oxford University Press, New York, 1937. 214 pp.

FIELD, MINNA, *Patients Are People:* A Medical-Social Approach to Prolonged Illness. Columbia University Press, New York, 1953. 244 pp.

FLEMING, CHARLOTTE M., *Adolescence:* Its Social Psychology. With an introduction to recent findings from the fields of anthropology, physiology, medicine, psychometrics, and sociometry. International Universities Press, New York, 1949. 262 pp.

FLEXNER, ABRAHAM, *Medical Education in the United States and Canada:* A Report to the Carnegie Foundation for the Advancement of Teaching. Bulletin 4, The Foundation, New York, 1910. 346 pp.

FLORENCE, PHILIP S., "Social Medicine Based on Social Statistics," *Nature*, vol. 153, March 25, 1944, pp. 363–365.

FLÜGEL, JOHN C., *Man, Morals and Society:* A Psycho-analytical Study. International Universities Press, New York, 1945. 328 pp.

The Psycho-analytic Study of the Family. International Psycho-analytic Press, New York, 1921. 259 pp.

FOOTE, NELSON N., "Identification as the Basis for a Theory of Motivation," *American Sociological Review*, vol. 16, February, 1951, pp. 14–21.

FORD, CLELLAN S., *Patterns of Sexual Behavior*. Harper and Bros., New York, 1951. 307 pp.

Smoke from Their Fires: The Life of a Kwakiuti Chief. Yale University Press, New Haven, 1941. 248 pp.

"Society, Culture, and the Human Organism," *Journal of General Psychology*, vol. 20, January, 1939, pp. 135–179.

"The Role of a Fijian Chief," *American Sociological Review*, vol. 3, August, 1938, pp. 541–550.

FORTUNE, REO F., *Sorcerers of Dobu*. E. P. Dutton and Co., New York, 1932. 318 pp.

FRANK, FRANK J., "The Situational Approach: A Reaction to Individualism," *Social Forces*, vol. 9, June, 1931, pp. 482–483.

FRANK, LAWRENCE K., "Man's Multidimensional Environment," *Scientific Monthly*, vol. 56, April, 1943, pp. 344–357.

Society as the Patient: Essays on Culture and Personality. Rutgers University Press, New Brunswick, N. J., 1948. 395 pp.

FREED, L. F., "Philosophy of Sociological Medicine," *South African Medical Journal*, vol. 22, March 13, 1948, pp. 190–198.

FROMM, ERICH, *Escape from Freedom*. Farrar and Rinehart, New York, 1941. 305 pp.

"Individual and Social Origins of Neurosis," *American Sociological Review*, vol. 9, August, 1944, pp. 380–384.

Man for Himself. Rinehart and Co., New York, 1947. 254 pp.

GALDSTON, IAGO, "Biodynamic Medicine Versus Psychosomatic Medicine," *Bulletin of the Menninger Clinic*, vol. 8, July, 1944, pp. 116–121.

"Social Medicine and the Epidemic Constitution," *Bulletin of the History of Medicine*, vol. 25, January–February, 1951, pp. 8–21.

"The Implications of Recent Advances in Medicine for Public Health" in *The Health of Eight Million:* Proceedings of the New York City Health Conference, 1951. 42 pp. Mayor's Committee on Management Survey of the City of New York, 1952, pp. 34–39.

The Meaning of Social Medicine. Commonwealth Fund, Harvard University Press, Cambridge, 1954. 178 pp.

GALDSTON, IAGO, editor, *Beyond the Germ Theory:* The Roles of Deprivation and Stress in Health and Disease. Health Education Council, New York, 1954. In preparation.

Social Medicine: Its Derivations and Objectives. Commonwealth Fund, New York, 1949. 294 pp.

GANTT, W. HORSLEY, *Experimental Basis for Neurotic Behavior*. Harper and Bros., New York, 1944. 211 pp.

"Principles of Nervous Breakdown—Schizokinesis and Autokinesis," *Annals* of the New York Academy of Sciences, vol. 56, February, 1953, pp. 143–163.

GARRETT, JAMES F., editor, *Psychological Aspects of Physical Disability*. United States Office of Vocational Rehabilitation, Washington, 1952. 194 pp.

GELLHORN, ERNST, *Autonomic Regulations:* Their Significance for Physiology, Psychology, and Neuropsychiatry. Interscience Publishers, New York, 1943. 373 pp.

GILDEA, EDWIN F., "Special Features of Personality Which Are Common to Certain Psychosomatic Disorders," *Psychosomatic Medicine*, vol. 11, September-October, 1949, pp. 273–281.

GILLIN, JOHN, "Acquired Drives in Culture Contact," *American Anthropologist*, vol. 44, October, 1942, pp. 545–554.

"Cultural Adjustment," *American Anthropologist*, vol. 46, October, 1944, pp. 429–447.

"Personality Formation from the Comparative Cultural Point of View" in *Personality in Nature, Society, and Culture*, edited by Clyde Kluckhohn and Henry A. Murray, 1948, pp. 164–175.

"Personality in Preliterate Societies," *American Sociological Review*, vol. 4, October, 1939, pp. 681–702.

"The Configuration Problem in Culture," *American Sociological Review*, vol. 1, June, 1936, pp. 373–386.

The Ways of Men: An Introduction to Anthropology. Appleton-Century Co., New York, 1948. 649 pp.

GILLIN, JOHN, AND G. E. NICHOLSON, "The Security Functions of Cultural Systems," *Social Forces*, vol. 30, December, 1951, pp. 179–184.

GILLIN, JOHN, AND VICTOR RAIMY, "Acculturation and Personality," *American Sociological Review*, vol. 5, June, 1940, pp. 371–380.

GOLDFRANK, ESTHER S., "Socialization, Personality, and the Structure of Pueblo Society: With Particular Reference to Hopi and Zuni," *American Anthropologist*, vol. 47, October, 1945, pp. 516–539.

GOLDHAMER, HERBERT, "Recent Development in Personality Studies," *American Sociological Review*, vol. 13, October, 1948, pp. 555–565.

GOLDSCHMIDT, WALTER R., "Ethics and the Structure of Society: An Ethnological Contribution to the Sociology of Knowledge," *American Anthropologist*, vol. 53, October, 1951, pp. 506–524.

"Social Class in America: A Critical Review," *American Anthropologist*, vol. 52, October, 1950, pp. 483–498.

GORDON, JOHN E., AND OTHERS, "The Biological and Social Sciences in an Epidemiology of Mental Disorder," *American Journal of the Medical Sciences*, vol. 223, March, 1952, pp. 316–343.

Gorer, Geoffrey, "Themes in Japanese Culture," *Transactions* of the New York Academy of Sciences, Series II, vol. 5, November, 1943, pp. 106–124.

Gottschalk, L. A., and others, "Psychological Conflict and Neuromuscular Tension: Preliminary Report on a Method as Applied to Rheumatoid Arthritis," *Proceedings* of the Association for Research in Nervous and Mental Disease, vol. 29, 1950, pp. 735–743.

Gottschalk, Louis R., and others, *The Use of Personal Documents in History, Anthropology and Sociology*. Social Science Research Council, Bulletin 53, New York, 1945. 243 pp.

Gough, Harrison G., "A New Dimension of Status: I. Development of a Personality Scale," *American Sociological Review*, vol. 13, August, 1948, pp. 401–409.

Grace, W. J., "Life Situations, Emotions and Chronic Ulcerative Colitis," *Proceedings* of the Association for Research in Nervous and Mental Disease, vol. 29, 1950, pp. 679–691.

Grace, W. J., and D. T. Graham, "Relationship of Specific Attitudes and Emotions to Certain Bodily Diseases," *Psychosomatic Medicine*, vol. 14, July–August, 1952, pp. 243–251.

Grace, W. J., and H. G. Wolff, "Treatment of Ulcerative Colitis," *Journal of the American Medical Association*, vol. 146, July 14, 1951, pp. 981–987.

Grace, W. J., Stewart Wolf, and H. G. Wolff, *The Human Colon:* An Experimental Study Based on Direct Observation of Four Fistulous Subjects. Paul B. Hoeber, Inc., New York, 1951. 239 pp.

Graham, D. T., "The Pathogenesis of Hives: Experimental Study of Life Situations, Emotions, and Cutaneous Vascular Reactions," *Proceedings* of the Association for Research in Nervous and Mental Disease, vol. 29, 1950, pp. 987–1009.

Grant, J. B., "Toward Health: Certain Trends," *Proceedings* of the Conference on Preventive Medicine and Health Economics, 1946, pp. 7–17. School of Public Health, University of Michigan.

Grant, R. T., R. S. B. Pearson, and W. J. Comeau, "Observations on Urticaria Provoked by Emotion, by Exercise and by Warming the Body," *Clinical Science*, vol. 2, July, 1936, pp. 253–272.

GREEN, ARNOLD W., "The Social Situation in Personality Theory," *American Sociological Review*, vol. 7, June, 1942, pp. 388–393.

GREENACRE, PHYLLIS, *Trauma, Growth, and Personality*. W. W. Norton and Co., New York, 1952. 328 pp.

GREENLEE, ROBERT F., "Medicine and Curing Practices of the Modern Florida Seminoles," *American Anthropologist*, vol. 46, July, 1944, pp. 317–328.

GREENWOOD, ERNEST, *Experimental Sociology:* A Study in Method. King's Crown Press, New York, 1944. 163 pp.

GREGG, ALAN, "The Future of Medicine," *Federation Bulletin*, vol. 23, January, 1937, pp. 5–12.

GROEN, JACQUES, *De Psychopathogenese van het Ulcus Ventriculi et Duodeni*. Scheltema and Holkema, Amsterdam, 1947. 125 pp.

"Psychogenesis and Psychotherapy of Ulcerative Colitis," *Psychosomatic Medicine*, vol. 9, May–June, 1947, pp. 151–174.

GRINKER, ROY R., AND FRED P. ROBBINS, *Psychosomatic Case Book*. Blakiston Co., New York, 1954. 323 pp.

HALL, J. K., AND OTHERS, editors, *One Hundred Years of American Psychiatry*. Columbia University Press, New York, 1944. 649 pp.

HALL, OSWALD, "Sociology Research in the Field of Medicine," *American Sociological Review*, vol. 16, October, 1951, pp. 639–644.

HALLIDAY, JAMES L., "Epidemiology and the Psychosomatic Affections," *Lancet*, vol. 2, August 10, 1946, pp. 185–191.

Psychosocial Medicine. W. W. Norton and Co., New York, 1948. 278 pp.

HALLOWELL, A. IRVING, "Cultural Factors in the Structuralization of Perception" in *Social Psychology at the Crossroads*, edited by John H. Rohrer and Muzafer Sherif, 1951, pp. 164–195.

"Fear and Anxiety as Cultural and Individual Variables in a Primitive Society," *Journal of Social Psychology*, vol. 9, February, 1938, pp. 25–47.

"Personality Structure and the Evolution of Man," *American Anthropologist*, vol. 52, April–June, 1950, pp. 159–173.

"Sin, Sex and Sickness in Saulteaux Belief," *British Journal of Medical Psychology*, vol. 18, July 24, 1939, pp. 191–197.

"Sociopsychological Aspects of Acculturation" in *The Science of Man in the World Crisis*, edited by Ralph Linton, 1945, pp. 171–200.

HALLOWELL, A. IRVING, *The Role of Conjuring in Saulteaux Society.* University of Pennsylvania Press, Philadelphia, 1942. 96 pp.

"The Social Function of Anxiety in a Primitive Society," *American Sociological Review*, vol. 6, December, 1941, pp. 869–881.

HAM, G. C., AND OTHERS, "Dynamic Aspects of the Personality Features and Reactions Characteristic of Patients with Graves Disease," *Proceedings* of the Association for Research in Nervous and Mental Disease, vol. 29, 1950, pp. 451–457.

HARING, DOUGLAS G., compiler, *Personal Character and Cultural Milieu:* A Collection of Readings. Rev. ed. Syracuse University Press, 1949. 670 pp.

HARLEY, GEORGE W., *Native African Medicine:* With Special Reference to Its Practice in the Mano Tribe of Liberia. Harvard University Press, Cambridge, 1941. 294 pp.

HARVEY, O. J., "An Experimental Approach to the Study of Status Relations in Informal Groups," *American Sociological Review*, vol. 18, August, 1953, pp. 357–367.

HATT, PAUL, "Class and Ethnic Attitudes," *American Sociological Review*, vol. 13, February, 1948, pp. 36–43.

HAVIGHURST, ROBERT J., AND HILDA TABA, *Adolescent Character and Personality.* John Wiley and Sons, New York, 1949. 315 pp.

HELD, ISIDORE W., AND A. A. GOLDBLOOM, *Peptic Ulcer:* Its Diagnosis and Treatment. Charles C. Thomas, Springfield, Ill., 1946. 382 pp.

HENDERSON, L. J., "Physician and Patient as a Social System," *New England Journal of Medicine*, vol. 212, May 2, 1935, pp. 819–823.

HENRY, W. E., "The Thematic Apperception Technique in the Study of Culture-Personality Relations," *Genetic Psychology Monographs*, vol. 35, February, 1947, pp. 3–155.

HERSKOVITS, MELVILLE J., *Man and His Works:* The Science of Cultural Anthropology. Alfred A. Knopf, Inc., New York, 1948. 678 pp. See especially "Culture and the Individual," pp. 43–60; "Social Organization," pp. 289–309; "The Ethnographic Laboratory," pp. 79–83; and "The Problem of Cultural Relativism," pp. 61–78.

HERTZLER, JOYCE O., *Social Institutions.* Rev. ed. University of Nebraska Press, Lincoln, 1946. 346 pp.

Hetzler, Stanley A., "An Investigation of the Distinctiveness of Social Classes," *American Sociological Review*, vol. 18, October, 1953, pp. 493–497.

Hilgard, Ernest R., "Human Motives and the Concept of the Self," *American Psychologist*, vol. 4, September, 1949, pp. 374–382.

Theories of Learning. Appleton-Century Co., New York, 1948. 409 pp.

Hill, Reuben L., *Families Under Stress:* Adjustment to the Crisis of War Separation and Reunions. Harper and Bros., New York, 1949. 443 pp.

Hill, Reuben L., editor, *The Family:* A Dynamic Interpretation. Dryden Press, New York, 1951. 637 pp. A revision of Willard Waller's *The Family*, 1938.

Hiller, Ernest T., *Social Relations and Structure:* A Study in Principles of Sociology. Harper and Bros., New York, 1947. 692 pp.

Hinkle, L. E., Jr., and Stewart Wolf, "Studies in Diabetes Mellitus: Changes in Glucose, Ketone, and Water Metabolism During Stress," *Proceedings* of the Association for Research in Nervous and Mental Disease, vol. 29, 1950, pp. 338–389.

Hinkle, L. E., Jr., Clifford J. Edwards, and Stewart Wolf, "Studies in Diabetic Mellitus: II. The Occurrence of a Diuresis in Diabetic Persons Exposed to Stressful Life Situations with Experimental Observations on its Relation to the Concentration of Glucose in Blood and Urine," *Journal of Clinical Investigation*, vol. 30, August, 1951, pp. 819–839.

"The Occurrence of Diuresis in Humans in Stressful Situations and Its Possible Relation to the Diuresis of Early Starvation," *Ibid.*, pp. 809–818.

Hinsie, Leland E., *The Person in the Body:* An Introduction to Psychosomatic Medicine. W. W. Norton and Co., New York, 1945. 263 pp.

Hobson, W., "What Is Social Medicine?" *British Medical Journal*, vol. 2, July 16, 1949, pp. 125–130.

Holden, Harold M., *Noses*. World Publishing Co., Cleveland, 1950. 252 pp.

HOLLINGSHEAD, AUGUST B., "A Re-examination of Ecological Theory," *Sociology and Social Research*, vol. 31, January, 1947, pp. 194–204.

Elmtown's Youth: The Impact of Social Classes on Adolescents. John Wiley and Sons, New York, 1949. 480 pp.

"Selected Characteristics of Classes in a Middle Western Community," *American Sociological Review*, vol. 12, August, 1947, pp. 385–395.

"The Concept of Social Control," *American Sociological Review*, vol. 6, April, 1941, pp. 217–224.

"Trends in Social Stratification: A Case Study," *American Sociological Review*, vol. 17, December, 1952, pp. 679–686.

HOLLINGSHEAD, AUGUST B., AND FREDERICK C. REDLICH, "Social Stratification and Psychiatric Disorders," *American Sociological Review*, vol. 18, April, 1953, pp. 163–169.

HOLMBERG, ALLAN R., *Nomads of the Long Bow:* The Seriono of Eastern Bolivia. Institute of Social Anthropology, Pub. 10. Government Printing Office, Washington, 1950. 104 pp.

HOLMES, THOMAS H., AND H. G. WOLFF, "Life Situations, Emotions and Backache," *Proceedings* of the Association for Research in Nervous and Mental Disease, vol. 29, 1950, pp. 750–772.

HOLMES, THOMAS H., AND OTHERS, "Life Situations, Emotions and Nasal Disease: Evidence on Summative Effects Exhibited in Patients with 'Hay Fever,'" *Proceedings* of the Association for Research in Nervous and Mental Disease, vol. 29, 1950, pp. 545–565.

The Nose: An Experimental Study of Reactions Within the Nose in Human Subjects During Varying Life Experiences. Charles C. Thomas, Springfield, Ill., 1949. 154 pp.

HOMANS, GEORGE C., *The Human Group*. Harcourt, Brace and Co., New York, 1950. 484 pp.

HONIGMANN, JOHN J., *Culture and Ethos of Kaska Society*. Yale University Publications in Anthropology, no. 40. Yale University Press, New Haven, 1949. 365 pp.

Culture and Personality. Harper and Bros., New York, 1954. 499 pp.

HOOTON, EARNEST A., *Up from the Ape*. Rev. ed. Macmillan Co., New York, 1947. 788 pp.

HORNEY, KAREN, *The Neurotic Personality of Our Time.* W. W. Norton and Co., New York, 1937. 299 pp.

HORST, PAUL, *The Prediction of Personal Adjustment.* Social Science Research Council, Bulletin 48, New York, 1941. 455 pp.

HOVLAND, CARL I., IRVING L. JANIS, AND HAROLD H. KELLEY, *Communication and Persuasion:* Psychological Studies of Opinion Change. Yale University Press, New Haven, 1953. 315 pp.

HSU, FRANCIS L. K., *Under the Ancestors' Shadow:* Chinese Culture and Personality. Columbia University Press, New York, 1948. 317 pp.

HU, HSIEN-CHIN, "The Chinese Concepts of 'Face,'" *American Anthropologist*, vol. 46, January, 1944, pp. 45–64.

HUGHES, EVERETT C., "Dilemmas and Contradictions of Status," *American Journal of Sociology*, vol. 50, March, 1945, pp. 353–359.

HULL, CLARK L., *Principles of Behavior:* An Introduction to Behavior Theory. Appleton-Century Co., New York, 1943. 422 pp.

HUNT, JOSEPH MCV., "An Instance of the Social Origin of Conflict Resulting in Psychoses," *American Journal of Orthopsychiatry*, vol. 8, January, 1938, pp. 158–164.

HUNT, JOSEPH MCV., editor, *Personality and the Behavior Disorders:* A Handbook Based on Experimental and Clinical Research. Ronald Press Co., New York, 1944. 2 vols.

JAMES, WILLIAM, *The Principles of Psychology.* Henry Holt and Co., New York, 1890. 2 vols.

JAMES, W. T., "Social Organization Among Dogs of Different Temperaments," *Journal of Comparative and Physiological Psychology*, vol. 44, February, 1951, pp. 71–77.

JENNINGS, DENYS, "Perforated Peptic Ulcer: Changes in Age-Incidence and Sex-Distribution in the Last 150 Years," *Lancet*, vol. 1, March 2 and 9, 1940, pp. 395–398, 444–447, 461.

JOHNSON, WINGATE M., "The Training of a General Practitioner," *The Diplomate*, vol. 22, May, 1950, pp. 193–199.

JONES, ERNEST, *The Life and Work of Sigmund Freud.* Vol. 1, Formative Years and the Great Discoveries, 1856–1900. Basic Books, New York, 1953. 428 pp.

JONES, MAXWELL, AND OTHERS, *The Therapeutic Community:* A New Treatment in Psychiatry. Basic Books, Inc., New York, 1953. 186 pp.

JOSSELYN, IRENE M., *Psychosocial Development of Children.* Family Service Association of America, New York, 1948. 134 pp.

KAHN, EUGEN, "Some Aspects of the Normal Personality Experiencing Disease," *Yale Journal of Biology and Medicine*, vol. 13, January, 1941, pp. 397–408.

KAHN, EUGEN, AND L. W. SIMMONS, "Problems of Middle Age," *Yale Review*, vol. 29, December, 1939, pp. 349–363.

KARDINER, ABRAM, "The Concept of Basic Personality Structure as an Operational Tool in the Social Sciences" in *The Science of Man in the World Crisis*, edited by Ralph Linton, 1945, pp. 107–122.

The Individual and His Society: The Psychodynamics of Primitive Social Organization. Columbia University Press, New York, 1939. 503 pp.

KARDINER, ABRAM, AND OTHERS, *The Psychological Frontiers of Society.* Columbia University Press, New York, 1945. 475 pp.

KAY, LILLIAN W., "Social Norms as Determinants in the Interpretation of Personal Experiences," *Journal of Social Psychology*, vol. 19, May, 1944, pp. 359–367.

KELLEY, HAROLD H., AND EDMUND H. VOLKART, "The Resistance to Change of Group-Anchored Attitudes," *American Sociological Review*, vol. 17, August, 1952, pp. 453–465.

KEMPF, EDWARD J., "Neuroses as Conditioned, Conflicting, Holistic, Attitudinal, Acquisitive-Avoidant Reactions," *Annals* of the New York Academy of Sciences, vol. 56, February, 1953, pp. 307–329.

"The Law of Attitude," *Journal of General Psychology*, vol. 32, January, 1945, pp. 81–102.

KERSHAW, JOHN D., *An Approach to Social Medicine.* Williams and Wilkins Co., Baltimore, 1946. 329 pp.

KEYS, ANCEL B., AND OTHERS, *The Biology of Human Starvation.* University of Minnesota Press, Minneapolis, 1950. 2 vols.

KLINEBERG, OTTO, "A Science of National Character," *Journal of Social Psychology*, vol. 19, February, 1944, pp. 147–162.

Social Psychology. Henry Holt and Co., New York, 1940. 570 pp.

KLUCKHOHN, CLYDE, *Mirror for Man:* The Relation of Anthropology to Modern Life. McGraw-Hill Book Co., New York, 1949. 313 pp. See especially "Personality in Culture: The Individual and the Group," pp. 196–227.

Navaho Witchcraft. Papers of the Peabody Museum of American Archaeology and Ethnology, Harvard University Press, Cambridge, 1944. 149 pp.

"Patterning as Exemplified in Navajo Culture" in *Language, Culture, and Personality*, edited by Leslie Spier and others, 1941, pp. 109–130.

"The Influence of Psychiatry on Anthropology in America During the Past One Hundred Years" in *One Hundred Years of American Psychiatry*, edited by J. K. Hall and others, 1944, pp. 589–617.

KLUCKHOHN, CLYDE, AND FLORENCE R. KLUCKHOHN, "American Culture: Generalized Orientations and Class Patterns" in *Conflicts of Power in Modern Culture*, edited by Lyman Bryson and others, 1947, pp. 106–128.

KLUCKHOHN, CLYDE, AND O. H. MOWRER, "Culture and Personality: A Conceptual Scheme," *American Anthropologist*, vol. 46, January, 1944, pp. 1–29.

KLUCKHOHN, CLYDE, AND HENRY A. MURRAY, editors, *Personality in Nature, Society and Culture*. Alfred A. Knopf, Inc., New York, 1948. 561 pp.

KOFFKA, KURT, *Principles of Gestalt Psychology*. Harcourt, Brace and Co., New York, 1935. 720 pp.

KROEBER, A. L., "Psychosis or Social Sanction," *Character and Personality*, vol. 8, March, 1940, pp. 204–215.

"So-called Social Science," *Journal of Social Philosophy*, vol. 1, July, 1936, pp. 317–340.

"The Concept of Culture in Science," *Journal of General Education*, vol. 3, April, 1949, pp. 182–196.

"The Societies of Primitive Man," *Biological Symposia*, vol. 8, 1942, pp. 205–216.

"The Superorganic," *American Anthropologist*, vol. 19, April–June, 1917, pp. 163–213.

KROEBER, A. L., editor, *Anthropology Today:* An Encyclopedic Inventory. University of Chicago Press, 1953. 928 pp.

KROGMAN, WILTON M., "The Man-Apes of South Africa," *Scientific American*, vol. 178, May, 1948, pp. 16–19.

KROPOTKIN, PETER A., *Mutual Aid:* A Factor of Evolution. 2d ed. Alfred A. Knopf, Inc., New York, 1916. 240 pp.

KROUT, MAURICE H., AND ROSS STAGNER, "Personality Development in Radicals: A Comparative Study," *Sociometry*, vol. 2, January, 1939, pp. 31–46.

KUNTZ, ALBERT, *Visceral Innervation and Its Relation to Personality*. Charles C. Thomas, Springfield, Ill., 1951. 160 pp.

KUO, Z. Y., "The Genesis of the Cat's Response to the Rat," *Journal of Comparative Psychology*, vol. 11, October, 1930, pp. 1–30.

LA BARRE, WESTON, "Primitive Psychotherapy in Native American Cultures: Peyotism and Confession," *Journal of Abnormal and Social Psychology*, vol. 42, July, 1947, pp. 294–309.

"The Cultural Basis of Emotions and Gestures," *Journal of Personality*, vol. 16, September, 1947, pp. 49–68.

The Peyote Cult. Yale University Publications in Anthropology, no. 19. Yale University Press, New Haven, 1938. 188 pp.

LADIEU, GLORIA, AND OTHERS, "Studies in Adjustment to Visible Injuries: Evaluation of Help by the Injured," *Journal of Abnormal and Social Psychology*, vol. 42, April, 1947, pp. 169–192.

LANDES, RUTH, *The Ojibwa Woman*. Columbia University Press, New York, 1938. 247 pp.

LANDIS, CARNEY, AND M. M. BOLLES, *Personality and Sexuality in the Physically Handicapped Woman*. Harper and Bros., New York, 1942. 171 pp.

LAPIERE, RICHARD T., "The Sociological Significance of Measurable Attitudes," *American Sociological Review*, vol. 3, April, 1938, pp. 175–182.

LAPIERE, RICHARD T., AND P. R. FARNSWORTH, *Social Psychology*. 3d ed. McGraw-Hill Book Co., New York, 1949. 626 pp.

LEAVELL, HUGH R., "Contributions of the Social Sciences to the Solution of Health Problems," *New England Journal of Medicine*, vol. 247, December 4, 1952, pp. 885–897.

"New Occasions Teach New Duties," *Public Health Reports*, vol. 68, July, 1953, pp. 687–692.

LEE, ALFRED McC., "Sociological Theory in Public Opinion and Attitude Studies," *American Sociological Review*, vol. 12, June, 1947, pp. 312–323.

"The Social Dynamics of the Physician's Status," *Psychiatry*, vol. 7, November, 1944, pp. 371–377.

LEIGHTON, ALEXANDER H., *Human Relations in a Changing World:* Observations on the Use of the Social Sciences. E. P. Dutton and Co., New York, 1949. 354 pp.

LEIGHTON, ALEXANDER H., AND DOROTHEA C. LEIGHTON, "Elements of Psychotherapy in Navaho Religion," *Psychiatry*, vol. 4, November, 1941, pp. 515–523.

Gregorio, the Hand-Trembler: A Psychobiological Personality Study of a Navaho Indian. Papers of the Peabody Museum of American Archaeology and Ethnology, Harvard University Press, Cambridge, 1949. 178 pp.

"Some Types of Uneasiness and Fear in a Navaho Indian Community," *American Anthropologist*, vol. 44, April, 1942, pp. 194–209.

The Navaho Door: An Introduction to Navaho Life. Harvard University Press, Cambridge, 1944. 149 pp.

LEIGHTON, DOROTHEA C., AND CLYDE KLUCKHOHN, *Children of the People:* The Navaho Individual and His Development. Harvard University Press, Cambridge, 1947. 277 pp.

LÉVI-STRAUSS, CLAUDE, "Social Structure" in *Anthropology Today*, edited by A. L. Kroeber, 1953, pp. 524–553.

LEWIN, KURT, *A Dynamic Theory of Personality*. McGraw-Hill Book Co., New York, 1935. 286 pp.

Field Theory in Social Science. Edited by Dorwin Cartwright. Harper and Bros., New York, 1951. 346 pp.

Resolving Social Conflicts: Selected Papers on Group Dynamics. Edited by Gertrud Weiss Lewin. Harper and Bros., New York, 1948. 230 pp.

LEWIN, KURT, AND OTHERS, "Patterns of Aggressive Behavior in Experimentally Created Social Climates," *Journal of Social Psychology*, vol. 10, May, 1939, pp. 271–299.

LEWIS, OSCAR, "Controls and Experiments in Field Work" in *Anthropology Today*, edited by A. L. Kroeber, 1953, pp. 452–475.

LINDEMANN, ERICH, "Modification in the Course of Ulcerative Colitis in Relationship to Changes in Life Situations and Reaction Patterns, *Proceedings* of the Association for Research in Nervous and Mental Disease, vol. 29, 1950, pp. 706–723.

"Psychiatric Problems in Conservative Treatment of Ulcerative Colitis," *Archives of Neurology and Psychiatry*, vol. 53, April, 1945, pp. 322–325.

"Symptomatology and Management of Acute Grief," *American Journal of Psychiatry*, vol. 101, September, 1944, pp. 141–148.

LINDESMITH, ALFRED R., AND ANSELM L. STRAUSS, "A Critique of Culture Personality Writings," *American Sociological Review*, vol. 15, October, 1950, pp. 587–600.

Social Psychology. Dryden Press, New York, 1949. 549 pp.

LINTON, RALPH, *Cultural Background of Personality*. Appleton-Century Co., New York, 1945. 157 pp.

"Culture, Society, and the Individual," *Journal of Abnormal and Social Psychology*, vol. 33, October, 1938, pp. 425–436.

"Problems of Status Personality" in *Culture and Personality*, edited by S. S. Sargent and M. W. Smith, 1949, pp. 163–173.

"The Effects of Culture on Mental and Emotional Processes," *Proceedings* of the Association for Research in Nervous and Mental Disease, vol. 19, 1939, pp. 293–304.

The Study of Man. Appleton-Century-Crofts, Inc., New York, 1936. 503 pp.

LINTON, RALPH, editor, *The Science of Man in the World Crisis*. Columbia University Press, New York, 1945. 532 pp.

LIPPERT, Julius, *Kulturgeschichte der Menschheit in ihrem organischen Aufbau*. F. Enke, Stuttgart, 1886. 2 vols.

LIPPITT, RONALD, "The Strategy of Sociopsychological Research" in *Experiments in Social Process:* A Symposium on Social Psychology, edited by J. G. Miller, 1950, pp. 17–30.

LONG, PERRIN H., "A Future for Preventive Medicine," *The Diplomate*, vol. 22, February, 1950, pp. 46–49.

LOWIE, ROBERT H., *A History of Ethnological Theory*. Farrar and Rinehart, New York, 1937. 296 pp.

"Social Organization," *Encyclopaedia of the Social Sciences*, vol. 14, 1934, pp. 141–148.

Social Organization. Rinehart and Co., New York, 1948. 465 pp.

LUMPKIN, KATHARINE DUPRE, *The Family:* A Study of Member Roles. University of North Carolina Press, Chapel Hill, 1933. 184 pp.

LYND, ROBERT S., AND HELEN M. LYND, *Middletown:* A Study in American Culture. Harcourt, Brace and Co., New York, 1929. 560 pp.

Middletown in Transition: A Study in Cultural Conflicts. Harcourt, Brace and Co., New York, 1937. 604 pp.

MACGREGOR, FRANCES C., "Some Psycho-social Problems Associated with Facial Deformities," *American Sociological Review*, vol. 16, October, 1951, pp. 629–638.

MACGREGOR, FRANCES C., AND OTHERS, *Facial Deformities and Plastic Surgery*, Charles C. Thomas, Springfield, Ill., 1953. 230 pp.

MACIVER, ROBERT M., *Community:* A Sociological Study. Macmillan Co., New York, 1931. 446 pp.

Social Causation. Ginn and Co., Boston, 1942. 414 pp.

Society: A Textbook of Sociology. Farrar and Rinehart, New York, 1937. 596 pp.

MACKENZIE, C. M., "Facial Deformity and Change in Personality Following Corrective Surgery," *Northwest Medicine*, vol. 43, August, 1944, pp. 230–231.

MADDOX, J. L., *The Medicine Man:* A Sociological Study of the Character and Evolution of Shamanism. Macmillan Co., New York, 1923. 330 pp.

MAIER, NORMAN R. F., *Frustration:* The Study of Behavior Without a Goal. McGraw-Hill Book Co., New York, 1949. 264 pp.

MALINOWSKI, BRONISLAW, *A Scientific Theory of Culture.* University of North Carolina Press, Chapel Hill, 1944. 228 pp.

Argonauts of the Western Pacific. E. P. Dutton and Co., New York, 1922. 527 pp.

Coral Gardens and Their Magic. American Book Co., New York, 1935. 2 vols.

Crime and Custom in Savage Society. Harcourt, Brace and Co., New York, 1926. 132 pp.

"Culture as a Determinant of Behavior," *Scientific Monthly*, vol. 43, November, 1936, pp. 440–449. Address delivered at Harvard Tercentenary Conference of Arts and Sciences, September, 1936.

MALINOWSKI, BRONISLAW, "Man's Culture and Man's Behavior," Parts I and II, *Sigma Xi Quarterly*, vols. 29 and 30, October, 1941, pp. 182–196, January, 1942, pp. 66–76.

Myth in Primitive Psychology. W. W. Norton and Co., New York, 1932. 94 pp.

Sex and Repression in Savage Society. Harcourt, Brace and Co., New York, 1927. 285 pp.

The Dynamics of Culture Change: An Inquiry into Race Relations in Africa. Edited by P. M. Kaberry. Yale University Press, New Haven, 1945. 171 pp.

The Father in Primitive Psychology. K. Paul, Trench, Trubner and Co., Ltd., London, 1927. 93 pp.

The Foundations of Faith and Morals. Oxford University Press, New York, 1936. 62 pp.

"The Group and the Individual in Functional Analysis," *American Journal of Sociology*, vol. 44, May, 1939, pp. 938–964.

The Sexual Life of Savages in Northwestern Melanesia. Horace Liveright Co., New York, 1929. 2 vols.

MALMO, ROBERT B., "Experimental Studies of Mental Patients Under Stress" in *Feelings and Emotions*, edited by Martin L. Reymert, 1950, pp. 169–180.

MANDELBAUM, DAVID G., "Social Trends and Personal Pressures: The Growth of a Culture Pattern" in *Language, Culture, and Personality*, edited by Leslie Spier and others, 1941, pp. 219–238.

MANDELBAUM, DAVID G., editor, *Selected Writings of Edward Sapir in Language, Culture, and Personality.* University of California Press, Berkeley, 1949. 617 pp.

MANGUS, ARTHUR R., "Mental Hygiene and Community Nursing," *Public Health Nursing*, vol. 39, September, 1947, pp. 426–432.

MANGUS, ARTHUR R., AND JOHN R. SEELEY, *Mental Health Needs.* Research Monographs, Division of Mental Hygiene, Ohio Department of Public Welfare, Columbus, 1950. 48 pp.

MANNHEIM, KARL, *Man and Society in an Age of Reconstruction.* Harcourt, Brace and Co., New York, 1940. 469 pp.

MASLOW, ABRAHAM H., "A Theory of Human Motivation," *Psychological Review*, vol. 50, July, 1943, pp. 370–376.

"Self-Actualizing People: A Study of Psychological Health" in *Personality:* Symposia on Topical Issues. *Values in Personality Research*, April, 1950, pp. 11–34. Grune and Stratton, Inc., New York.

MAY, ROLLO, *The Meaning of Anxiety*. Ronald Press Co., New York, 1950. 376 pp.

McNEMAR, QUINN, "Opinion-Attitude Methodology," *Psychological Bulletin*, vol. 43, July, 1946, pp. 289–374.

MEAD, GEORGE H., *Mind, Self and Society:* From the Standpoint of a Social Behaviorist. University of Chicago Press, 1934. 401 pp.

MEAD, MARGARET, *Growing Up in New Guinea:* A Comparative Study of Primitive Education. William Morrow and Co., New York, 1930. 372 pp.

Sex and Temperament in Three Primitive Societies. William Morrow and Co., New York, 1934. 335 pp.

"Social Change and the Cultural Surrogates," *Journal of Educational Sociology*, vol. 14, October, 1940, pp. 92–109.

"The Concept of Culture and the Psychosomatic Approach," *Psychiatry*, vol. 10, February, 1947, pp. 57–76.

"The Implications of Culture Change for Personality Development," *American Journal of Orthopsychiatry*, vol. 17, October, 1947, pp. 633–646.

"The Use of Primitive Material in a Study of Personality," *Character and Personality*, vol. 3, September, 1935, pp. 1–16.

MEAD, MARGARET, AND F. C. MACGREGOR, *Growth and Culture:* A Photographic Study of Balinese Childhood. G. P. Putnam's Sons, New York, 1951. 239 pp.

MEGGERS, BETTY J., "Recent Trends in American Ethnology," *American Anthropologist*, vol. 48, April, 1946, pp. 176–214.

MELENEY, H. E., "Preventive Medical Services for the Family," *Milbank Memorial Fund Quarterly*, vol. 27, July, 1949, pp. 251–259.

"Preventive Medicine in Tomorrow's World," *Journal of the Association of American Medical Colleges*, vol. 25, March, 1950, pp. 102–110.

MELENEY, H. E., "The Next Ten Years in Medicine: Social and Environmental Factors in the Practice of Medicine," *New York Medicine*, vol. 3, April 20, 1947, pp. 15–18.

MENNINGER, KARL A., "Changing Concepts of Disease," *Annals of Internal Medicine*, vol. 29, August, 1948, pp. 318–325.

MERTON, ROBERT K., "Bureaucratic Structure and Personality," *Social Forces*, vol. 18, May, 1940, pp. 560–568.

Mass Persuasion: The Social Psychology of a War Bond Drive. Harper and Bros., New York, 1946. 210 pp.

Social Theory and Social Structure: Toward the Codification of Theory and Research. The Free Press, Glencoe, Ill., 1949. 423 pp.

MILBANK MEMORIAL FUND, *Backgrounds of Social Medicine*. The Fund, New York, 1949. 202 pp.

Interrelations Between the Social Environment and Psychiatric Disorders: Papers Presented at the 1952 Conference of the Fund. The Fund, 1953. 265 pp.

Research in Public Health: Papers Presented at the 1951 Conference of the Fund. The Fund, 1952. 279 pp.

MILLER, JAMES G., editor, *Experiments in Social Process:* A Symposium on Social Psychology. 2d ed. McGraw-Hill Book Co., New York, 1950. 205 pp.

MILLER, NEAL E., AND JOHN DOLLARD, *Social Learning and Imitation*. Yale University Press, New Haven, 1941. 341 pp.

MILLS, THEODORE M., "Power Relations in Three-Person Groups," *American Sociological Review*, vol. 18, August, 1953, pp. 351–357.

MINOT, GEORGE R., "Investigation and Teaching in the Field of the Social Component of Medicine," *Bulletin* of the American Association of Medical Social Workers, vol. 10, April, 1937, pp.9–18.

"Medical Social Aspects in Practice," *Archives of Internal Medicine*, vol. 54, July, 1934, pp. 1–10.

MITTLEMANN, BELA, AND H. G. WOLFF, "Emotions and Gastroduodenal Function: Experimental Studies on Patients with Gastritis, Duodenitis, and Peptic Ulcer," *Psychosomatic Medicine*, vol. 4, January, 1942, pp. 5–61.

MOORE, ROBERT A., "The Physician and the Law," *The Diplomate*, vol. 22, May, 1950, pp. 168–176.

MORGAN, CLIFFORD T., *Physiological Psychology*. McGraw-Hill Book Co., New York, 1943. 623 pp.

MORGAN, WILLIAM, "Navaho Treatment of Sickness: Diagnosticians," *American Anthropologist*, vol. 33, July, 1931, pp. 390–402.

MOWRER, ERNEST R., *Family Disorganization*. University of Chicago Press, 1927. 317 pp.

"Social Crises and Social Disorganization," *American Sociological Review*, vol. 15, February, 1950, pp. 60–66.

MOWRER, ORVAL H., *Learning Theory and Personality Dynamics*. Ronald Press Co., New York, 1950. 776 pp.

MOWRER, ORVAL H., editor, *Psychotherapy:* Theory and Research. Ronald Press Co., New York, 1953. 700 pp.

MOWRER, ORVAL H., AND CLYDE KLUCKHOHN, "Dynamic Theory of Personality" in *Personality and the Behavior Disorders*, edited by Joseph McV. Hunt, 1944, vol. 1, pp. 69–135.

MÜHLMANN, W. E., *Geschichte der Anthropologie*. Universitäts-Verlag Bonn, Bonn, 1948. 274 pp.

MUKHERJEE, RAMKRISHNA, "The Economic Structure and Social Life in Six Villages of Bengal," *American Sociological Review*, vol. 14, June, 1949, pp. 415–425.

MUNN, NORMAN L., *Psychology:* The Fundamentals of Human Adjustment. Edited by Leonard Carmichael. Houghton Mifflin Co., Boston, 1946. 497 pp.

MURCHISON, CARL A., *A Handbook of Social Psychology*. Clark University Press, Worcester, Mass., 1935. 1195 pp.

MURDOCK, GEORGE P., "Bronislaw Malinowski," *American Anthropologist*, vol. 45, July, 1943, pp. 441–451.

Social Structure. Macmillan Co., New York, 1949. 387 pp.

"The Science of Culture," *American Anthropologist*, vol. 34, April, 1932, pp. 200–215.

MURDOCK, GEORGE P., editor, *Studies in the Science of Society*. Yale University Press, New Haven, 1937. 555 pp.

MURDOCK, GEORGE P., AND OTHERS, *Outline of Cultural Materials*. Yale University Press, New Haven, 1945. 56 pp.

MURPHY, GARDNER, *Personality:* A Biosocial Approach to Origins and Structure. Harper and Bros., New York, 1947. 999 pp.

Murphy, Gardner, and Rensis Likert, *Public Opinion and the Individual.* Harper and Bros., New York, 1938. 316 pp.

Murray, Henry A., *Explorations in Personality.* Oxford University Press, New York, 1938. 761 pp.

Myers, Jerome K., "Assimilation to the Ecological and Social Systems of a Community," *American Sociological Review*, vol. 15, June, 1950, pp. 367–372.

Nadel, Siegfried F., *The Foundations of Social Anthropology.* The Free Press, Glencoe, Ill., 1951. 426 pp.

Nelson, Erland, "Attitudes," *Journal of General Psychology*, vol. 21, October, 1939, pp. 367–436.

Newcomb, Theodore M., "Community Roles in Attitude Formation," *American Sociological Review*, vol. 7, October, 1942, pp. 621–630.

Social Psychology. Dryden Press, New York, 1950. 690 pp.

Newcomb, Theodore M., and George Svehla, "Intra-Family Relationships in Attitude," *Sociometry*, vol. 1, July-October, 1937, pp. 180–205.

Ogburn, William F., *Social Change:* With Respect to Culture and Original Nature. Rev. ed. Viking Press, New York, 1950. 373 pp.

O'Hara, Dwight, "Today's Trends in Medical Education," *The Diplomate*, vol. 22, December, 1950, pp. 291–296.

Opler, Morris E., *An Apache Life-Way:* The Economic, Social, and Religious Institutions of the Chiricahua Indians. University of Chicago Press, 1941. 500 pp.

"Cultural Alternatives and Educational Theory," *Harvard Educational Review*, vol. 17, Winter, 1947, pp. 28–44.

"Cultural Anthropology: An Application of the Theory of Themes in Culture," *Journal* of the Washington Academy of Sciences, vol. 36, 1946, pp. 137–166.

"Themes as Dynamic Forces in Culture," Parts I and II, *American Journal of Sociology*, vols. 51 and 52, November, 1945, pp. 198–206, July, 1946, pp. 43–44.

"Three Types of Variation and Their Relation to Culture Change" in *Language, Culture, and Personality*, edited by Leslie Spier and others, 1941, pp. 146–157.

PARK, ROBERT E., "Personality and Cultural Conflict," *Publications of the American Sociological Society*, vol. 25, 1931, pp. 95–110.

PARSONS, TALCOTT, "Age and Sex in the Social Structure of the United States," *American Sociological Review*, vol. 7, October, 1942, pp. 604–616.

"Personality and Social Structure" in *Personality and Political Crisis*, edited by Alfred H. Stanton and Stewart E. Perry, 1951, pp. 61–80.

The Social System. The Free Press, Glencoe, Ill., 1951. 575 pp.

PARSONS, TALCOTT, AND EDWARD A. SHILS, editors, *Toward a General Theory of Action*. Harvard University Press, Cambridge, 1951. 506 pp.

PAUL, BENJAMIN D., "Mental Disorders and Self-Regulating Processes in Culture: A Guatemalan Illustration" in *Interrelations Between the Social Environment and Psychiatric Disorders:* Papers Presented at the 1952 Conference of the Milbank Memorial Fund, pp. 51–68.

PAUL, J. R., "Preventive Medicine at Yale University School of Medicine, 1940–1949," *Yale Journal of Biology and Medicine*, vol. 22, January, 1950, pp. 199–211.

PAVLOV, IVAN P., *Conditioned Reflexes:* An Investigation of the Physiological Activity of the Cerebral Cortex. Translated by G. V. Anrep. Oxford University Press, New York, 1927. 430 pp.

Lectures on Conditioned Reflexes. Translated by W. H. Gantt. International Publishers, New York, 1928. 2 vols.

PEARSE, INNES H., AND L. H. CROCKER, *The Peckham Experiment:* A Study in the Living Structure of Society. Yale University Press, New Haven, 1945. 333 pp.

PEMBERTON, JOHN, "Possible Developments in Social Medicine," *British Medical Journal*, vol. 2, December 11, 1943, pp. 754–755.

PINNER, MAX, AND B. F. MILLER, editors, *When Doctors Are Patients*. W. W. Norton and Co., New York, 1952. 364 pp.

PLANT, JAMES S., *Personality and the Cultural Pattern*. Commonwealth Fund, New York, 1937. 432 pp.

The Envelope: A Study of the Impact of the World Upon the Child. Commonwealth Fund, New York, 1950. 299 pp.

POLLAK, OTTO, *Social Adjustment in Old Age*. Social Science Research Council, Bulletin 59, New York, 1948. 199 pp.

POLLAK, OTTO, AND COLLABORATORS, *Social Science and Psychotherapy for Children*. Russell Sage Foundation, New York, 1952. See especially "Culture and Culture Conflict in Psychotherapy" written in collaboration with Yonata Feldman, pp. 101–132.

PRICHARD, J. S., AND OTHERS, "Effects of Stress and Results of Medication in Different Personalities with Parkinson's Disease," *Journal of Psychosomatic Medicine*, vol. 13, March-April, 1951, pp. 106–111.

PROCEEDINGS of the Association for Research in Nervous and Mental Disease: *Life Stress and Bodily Disease*. Williams and Wilkins Co., Baltimore, vol. 29, 1950. 1135 pp.

PRUGH, D. G., "Variations in Attitudes, Behavior and Feeling-States as Exhibited in the Play of Children During Modifications in the Course of Ulcerative Colitis," *Proceedings* of the Association for Research in Nervous and Mental Disease, vol. 29, 1950, pp. 692–705.

QUEEN, STUART A., "Some Problems of the Situational Approach," *Social Forces*, vol. 9, June, 1931, pp. 480–481.

QUEEN, STUART A., AND J. B. ADAMS, *The Family in Various Cultures*. J. B. Lippincott Co., Philadelphia, 1952. 280 pp.

RADCLIFFE-BROWN, ALFRED R., *Structure and Function in Primitive Society*. The Free Press, Glencoe, Ill., 1952. 219 pp.

RADIN, PAUL, editor, *Crashing Thunder:* The Autobiography of an American Indian. D. Appleton Co., New York, 1926. 202 pp. Published in 1920 as Part I of *The Autobiography of a Winnebago Indian*, in the University of California series in American Archaeology and Ethnology, vol. 16, no. 7.

RAPPLEYE, WILLARD C., "The Physician in Modern Society," *The Diplomate*, vol. 22, November, 1950, pp. 245–251.

RAY, BRONSON S., AND A. DALE CONSOLE, "Bodily Adjustments in Man During Stress in the Absence of Most Visceral Afferents and Sympathetic Nervous System Regulation," *Proceedings of* the Association for Research in Nervous and Mental Disease, vol. 29, 1950, pp. 114–120.

"Evaluation of Total Sympathectomy," *Annals of Surgery*, vol. 130, October, 1949, pp. 652–673.

REDFIELD, ROBERT, *The Folk Culture of Yucatan.* University of Chicago Press, 1941. 416 pp.

"The Folk Society," *American Journal of Sociology*, vol. 52, January, 1947, pp. 293–308.

The Primitive World and Its Transformations. Cornell University Press, Ithaca, N. Y., 1953. 185 pp.

REDLICH, F. C., "The Concept of Normality," *American Journal of Psychotherapy*, vol. 6, July, 1952, pp. 551–576.

REINHARDT, JAMES M., "Personality Traits and the Situation," *American Sociological Review*, vol. 2, August, 1937, pp. 492–500.

REYHER, REBECCA H., *Zulu Woman.* Columbia University Press, New York, 1948. 281 pp.

REYMERT, MARTIN L., editor, *Feelings and Emotions.* McGraw-Hill Book Co., New York, 1950. 603 pp.

RICHARDSON, HENRY B., *Patients Have Families.* Commonwealth Fund, New York, 1945. 408 pp.

RIVERS, WILLIAM H. R., *Medicine, Magic and Religion.* K. Paul, London, 1924. 146 pp.

ROBERTS, JOHN M., *Three Navaho Households.* Papers of the Peabody Museum of American Archaeology and Ethnology, Harvard University Press, Cambridge, 1952. 88 pp.

ROBINSON, G. CANBY, "Proper Attention to the Role of Emotional and Social Factors in Illness as a New Step in Public Health," *Milbank Memorial Fund Quarterly*, vol. 23, January, 1945, pp. 20–27.

The Patient as a Person: A Study of the Social Aspects of Illness. Commonwealth Fund, New York, 1939. 437 pp.

ROBINSON, W. S., "Ecological Correlations and the Behavior of Individuals," *American Sociological Review*, vol. 15, June, 1950, pp. 351–357.

ROEMER, M. I., "Relationship of Social Medicine to the Social Sciences," *Journal of the Association of American Medical Colleges*, vol. 23, September, 1948, pp. 324–329.

ROETHLISBERGER, FRITZ J., AND W. J. DICKSON, *Management and the Worker.* Harvard University Press, Cambridge, 1939. 615 pp.

ROGERS, C. R., "Some Observations on the Organization of Personality," *American Psychologist*, vol. 2, September, 1947, pp. 358–368.

RÓHEIM, GÉZA, *The Origin and Function of Culture*. Nervous and Mental Disease Monographs, New York, 1943. 108 pp.

ROHRER, JOHN H., AND MUZAFER SHERIF, editors, *Social Psychology at the Crossroads*. Harper and Bros., New York, 1951. 437 pp.

ROMANO, JOHN, "Emotional Components of Illness," *Connecticut State Medical Journal*, vol. 7, January, 1943, pp. 22–25.

"Patients' Attitudes and Behavior in Ward Round Teaching," *Journal of the American Medical Association*, vol. 117, August 30, 1941, pp. 664–667.

ROSE, ARNOLD M., "Conditions of the Social Science Experiment," *American Sociological Review*, vol. 13, October, 1948, pp. 616–619.

ROSEN, GEORGE, "The Ideal of Social Medicine in America," *Canadian Medical Association Journal*, vol. 61, September, 1949, pp. 316–323.

"What Is Social Medicine? Genetic Analysis of the Concept," *Bulletin of the History of Medicine*, vol. 21, September-October, 1947, pp. 674–733.

ROSEN, HAROLD, AND THEODORE LIDZ, "Emotional Factors in the Precipitation of Recurrent Diabetic Acidosis," *Psychosomatic Medicine*, vol. 11, July–August, 1949, pp. 211–215.

RUESCH, JURGEN, "Social Technique, Social Status, and Social Change in Illness" in *Personality in Nature, Society and Culture*, edited by Clyde Kluckhohn and Henry A. Murray, 1948, pp. 117–130.

RUESCH, JURGEN, AND GREGORY BATESON, *Communication:* The Social Matrix of Psychiatry. W. W. Norton and Co., New York, 1951. 314 pp.

RUESCH, JURGEN, ANNEMARIE JACOBSON, AND MARTIN B. LOEB, *Acculturation and Illness*. Psychological Monographs: General and Applied, vol. 62, no. 5, 1948. 40 pp.

RYLE, J. A., "Social Medicine: Its Meaning and Its Scope," *Milbank Memorial Fund Quarterly*, vol. 22, January, 1944, pp. 58–71.

SANAI, MAHMOUD, "An Experimental Study of Social Attitudes," *Journal of Social Psychology*, vol. 34, November, 1951, pp. 235–264.

SAND, RENÉ, *Health and Human Progress:* An Essay in Sociological Medicine. Translated by C. F. Marshall. Macmillan Co., New York, 1936. 278 pp.

The Advance to Social Medicine. Staples Press, New York, 1952. 655 pp.

SAPIR, EDWARD, "Cultural Anthropology and Psychiatry," *Journal of Abnormal and Social Psychology*, vol. 27, October, 1932, pp. 229–242.

"Culture, Genuine and Spurious," *American Journal of Sociology*, vol. 29, January, 1924, pp. 401–429.

"Personality," *Encyclopaedia of the Social Sciences*, vol. 12, 1934, pp. 85–88.

"The Emergence of the Concept of Personality in a Study of Cultures," *Journal of Social Psychology*, vol. 5, August, 1934, pp. 408–415.

"The Unconscious Patterning of Behavior in Society" in *The Unconscious:* A Symposium, edited by Ethel S. Dummer, 1928, pp. 114–142.

SARGENT, HELEN, "Projective Methods: Their Origins, Theory and Application," *Psychological Bulletin*, vol. 42, May, 1945, pp. 257–293.

SARGENT, S. STANSFELD, AND M. W. SMITH, editors, *Culture and Personality*. Viking Fund, New York, 1949. 219 pp.

SAUL, LEON J., *Emotional Maturity:* The Development and Dynamics of Personality. J. B. Lippincott Co., Philadelphia, 1947. 338 pp.

SCARFF, J. E., "Reaction to Life Stresses Following Unilateral Prefrontal Lobectomy or Lobotomy," *Proceedings* of the Association for Research in Nervous and Mental Disease, vol. 29, 1950, pp. 121–126.

SCHERMERHORN, RICHARD A., "Social Psychiatry," *The Antioch Review*, vol. 13, March, 1953, pp. 67–85.

SCHJELDERUP-EBBE, THORLEIF, "Social Behavior of Birds" in *A Handbook of Social Psychology*, edited by Carl A. Murchison, 1935, pp. 947–972.

SCHNEIDER, DAVID M., "The Social Dynamics of Physical Disability in Army Basic Training," *Psychiatry*, vol. 10, August, 1947, pp. 323–333.

SCHNEIDER, LOUIS, "Some Psychiatric Views on 'Freedom' and the Theory of Social Systems," *Psychiatry*, vol. 12, August, 1949, pp. 251–264.

SCHNEIRLA, THEODORE C., "Problems in the Biopsychology of Social Organization," *Journal of Abnormal Psychology*, vol. 41, October, 1946, pp. 385–402.

SCHWARTZ, A. B., "The Relationship of Home and Hospital in the Management of Sick Children," *Journal of Pediatrics*, vol. 4, April, 1934, pp. 431–435.

SEARS, ROBERT R., "Ordinal Position in the Family as a Psychological Variable," *American Sociological Review*, vol. 15, June, 1950, pp. 397–401.

SEIDENFELD, MORTON A., *Psychological Aspects of Medical Care*. Charles C. Thomas, Springfield, Ill., 1949. 60 pp.

SELIGMAN, CHARLES G., "Anthropological Perspective and Psychological Theory," *Journal of Royal Anthropological Institute of Great Britain and Ireland*, vol. 62, 1932, pp. 193–228.

"Anthropology and Psychology," *Journal of Royal Anthropological Institute*, vol. 54, 1924, pp. 13–46.

"The Unconscious in Relation to Anthropology," *British Journal of Psychology*, vol. 18, April, 1928, pp. 373–387.

SELYE, HANS, "The General Adaptation Syndrome and the Diseases of Adaptation," *Journal of Clinical Endocrinology*, vol. 6, February, 1946, pp. 117–230.

The Physiology and Pathology of Exposure to Stress. Acta, Inc., Montreal, 1950. 1025 pp.

SHAFFER, LAURANCE F., *The Psychology of Adjustment:* An Objective Approach to Mental Hygiene. Houghton Mifflin Co., Boston, 1936. 600 pp.

SHELDON, WILLIAM H., *Varieties of Temperament:* A Psychology of Constitutional Differences. Harper and Bros., New York, 1942. 520 pp.

SHERIF, MUZAFER, *An Outline of Social Psychology*. Harper and Bros., New York, 1948. 479 pp.

"Some Methodological Remarks Related to Experimentation in Social Psychology," *International Journal of Opinion and Attitude Research*, vol. 1, June, 1947, pp. 71–93.

SHERIF, MUZAFER, AND HADLEY CANTRIL, *The Psychology of Ego-Involvements*. John Wiley and Sons, New York, 1947. 525 pp.

SHILS, EDWARD A., *The Present State of American Sociology*. The Free Press, Glencoe, Ill., 1948. 64 pp.

SHRYOCK, RICHARD H., *American Medical Research, Past and Present*. Commonwealth Fund, New York, 1947. 350 pp.

The Development of Modern Medicine: An Interpretation of the Social and Scientific Factors Involved. Rev. and enl. ed. Alfred A. Knopf, Inc., New York, 1947. 456 pp.

"The Historian Looks at Medicine," *Bulletin of the History of Medicine*, vol. 5, December, 1937, pp. 887–894.

SIGERIST, HENRY E., *A History of Medicine*. Vol. 1, Primitive and Archaic Medicine. Oxford University Press, New York, 1951. 564 pp.

Man and Medicine. W. W. Norton and Co., New York, 1932. 340 pp.

SIMMONS, LEO W., "A Frame of Reference for Family Research in Problems of Medical Care," in *Research in Public Health:* Papers Presented at the 1951 Conference of the Milbank Memorial Fund, pp. 163–181.

"A Prospectus for Field-Research in the Position and Treatment of the Aged in Primitive and Other Societies," *American Anthropologist*, vol. 47, July, 1945, pp. 433–438.

"Social Participation of the Aged in Different Cultures," *Annals* of the American Academy of Political and Social Science, vol. 279, January, 1952, pp. 43–51.

"Statistical Correlations in the Science of Society" in *Studies in the Science of Society*, edited by George P. Murdock, 1937, pp. 495–517.

"The Dynamic Psychology of the Group and the Shaping of Individual Behavior" in *Psychological Dynamics of Health Education:* Proceedings of Eastern States Health Education Conference, 1950. Columbia University Press, New York, 1951, pp. 55–68.

SIMMONS, LEO W., "The Relation Between the Decline of Anxiety-Inducing and Anxiety-Resolving Factors in a Deteriorating Culture and Its Relevance to Bodily Disease," *Proceedings* of the Association for Research in Nervous and Mental Disease, vol. 29, 1950, pp. 127–136.

The Role of the Aged in Primitive Society. Yale University Press, New Haven, 1945. 317 pp.

SIMMONS, LEO W., editor, *Sun Chief:* The Autobiography of a Hopi Indian. Yale University Press, New Haven, 1942. 460 pp.

SINNOTT, EDMUND W., *Cell and Psyche:* The Biology of Purpose. University of North Carolina Press, Chapel Hill, 1950. 121 pp.

"The Biology of Purpose," *American Journal of Orthopsychiatry*, vol. 22, July, 1952, pp. 457–468.

SIRJAMAKI, JOHN, *The American Family in the Twentieth Century.* Harvard University Press, Cambridge, 1953. 227 pp.

SLOTKIN, JAMES S., *Social Anthropology:* The Science of Human Society and Culture. Macmillan Co., New York, 1950. 604 pp.

SMILLIE, W. G., "Medicine as a Social Instrument: Preventive Medicine," *New England Journal of Medicine*, vol. 244, March, 1951, pp. 329–333.

SPENCE, J. C., *The Care of Children in Hospitals.* U.S. Children's Bureau, Washington, 1948. 16 pp.

SPENCER, HERBERT, *Principles of Sociology.* D. Appleton Co., New York, 1896. 3 vols.

SPIER, LESLIE, A. I. HALLOWELL, AND S. S. NEWMAN, *Language, Culture, and Personality:* Essays in Memory of Edward Sapir. Sapir Memorial Education Fund, Menasha, Wis., 1941. 298 pp.

STAGNER, ROSS, *Psychology of Personality.* 2d ed. McGraw-Hill Book Co., New York, 1948. 485 pp.

"Studies of Aggressive Social Attitudes. III, Role of Personal and Family Scores," *Journal of Social Psychology*, vol. 20, August, 1944, pp. 109–140.

STALLYBRASS, C. O., "Social Medicine and the Comprehensive Medical Service," *Medical Officer*, vol. 72, September 30, 1944, pp. 109–112.

STANTON, ALFRED H., AND MORRIS S. SCHWARTZ, "Medical Opinion and the Social Context in the Mental Hospital," *Psychiatry*, vol. 12, August, 1949, pp. 243–249.

STANTON, ALFRED H., AND STEWART E. PERRY, editors, *Personality and Political Crisis:* New Perspectives from Social Science and Psychiatry for the Study of War and Politics. The Free Press, Glencoe, Ill., 1951. 260 pp.

STEARNS, A. WARREN, "Integration of Medical Science and Sociology," *Journal of Nervous and Mental Disease*, vol. 103, June, 1946, pp. 612–625.

STERN, BERNHARD J., *American Medical Practice in the Perspectives of a Century*. Commonwealth Fund, New York, 1945. 156 pp.

"Concerning the Distinction Between the Social and the Cultural," *Social Forces*, vol. 8, December, 1929, pp. 264–271.

Medical Services by Government: Local, State, and Federal. Commonwealth Fund, New York, 1946. 208 pp.

Medicine in Industry. Commonwealth Fund, New York, 1946. 209 pp.

Society and Medical Progress. Princeton University Press, Princeton, 1941. 264 pp.

STEVENSON, GEORGE S., editor, *Administrative Medicine:* Transactions of the First Conference on Administrative Medicine, March 9–11, 1953. Josiah Macy, Jr. Foundation, New York, 176 pp.

STEWARD, JULIAN H., "Levels of Sociocultural Integration: An Operational Concept," *Southwestern Journal of Anthropology*, vol. 7, Winter, 1951, pp. 374–390.

STIEGLITZ, EDWARD J., *A Future for Preventive Medicine*. Commonwealth Fund, New York, 1945. 77 pp.

STONE, ERIC, *Medicine Among the American Indians*. Paul B. Hoeber, Inc., New York, 1932. 139 pp.

STONEQUIST, EVERETT V., *The Marginal Man:* A Study in Personality and Culture Conflict. Charles Scribner's Sons, New York, 1937. 228 pp.

STRAUSS, ANSELM L., "The Concept of Attitude in Social Psychology," *Journal of Psychology*, vol. 19, April, 1945, pp. 329–339.

SULLIVAN, HARRY STACK, *Conceptions of Modern Psychiatry.* William Alanson White Psychiatric Foundation, Washington, 1947. 147 pp.

"Psychiatric Aspects of Morale," *American Journal of Sociology,* vol. 47, November, 1941, pp. 277–301.

SUMNER, WILLIAM G., *Folkways.* Ginn and Co., Boston, 1906. 692 pp.

SUMNER, WILLIAM G., AND A. G. KELLER, *The Science of Society.* Yale University Press, New Haven, 1927. 4 vols.

SZASZ, THOMAS S., "Psychosomatic Aspects of Salivary Activity. I. Hypersalivation in Patients with Peptic Ulcer," *Proceedings* of the Association for Research in Nervous and Mental Disease, vol. 29, 1950, pp. 647–655.

TAX, SOL, AND OTHERS, editors, *An Appraisal of Anthropology Today.* International Symposium of Anthropology, New York, 1952. University of Chicago Press, 1953. 395 pp.

THOMAS, W. I., *Primitive Behavior:* An Introduction to the Social Sciences. McGraw-Hill Book Co., New York, 1937. 847 pp.

Social Behavior and Personality: Contributions to Theory and Social Research. Edited by Edmund H. Volkart. Social Science Research Council, New York, 1951. 338 pp.

"The Configurations of Personality" in *The Unconscious:* A Symposium, edited by Ethel S. Dummer, 1928, pp. 143–177.

THOMAS, W. I., AND FLORIAN ZNANIECKI, *The Polish Peasant in Europe and America.* Richard Y. Badger, Boston, 1918–1920. 5 vols. Alfred A. Knopf, Inc., New York, 1927. 2 vols.

THOMPSON, LAURA M., "Attitudes and Acculturation," *American Anthropologist,* vol. 50, April, 1948, pp. 200–215.

THOMPSON, LAURA M., AND ALICE JOSEPH, "White Pressures on Indian Personality and Culture," *American Journal of Sociology,* vol. 53, July, 1947, pp. 17–22.

THORNTON, JANET, AND MARJORIE KNAUTH, *The Social Component in Medical Care:* A Study of One Hundred Cases from the Presbyterian Hospital in the City of New York. Columbia University Press, New York, 1937. 411 pp.

THURNWALD, RICHARD, "The Psychology of Acculturation," *American Anthropologist,* vol. 34, October, 1932, pp. 557–569.

Thurstone, Louis L., and E. J. Chave, *The Measurement of Attitude.* University of Chicago Press, 1929. 96 pp.

Treuting, Theodore F., and Herbert S. Ripley, "Life Situations, Emotions and Bronchial Asthma," *Journal of Nervous and Mental Disease,* vol. 108, November, 1948, pp. 380–398.

Tudor, Gwen E., "A Sociopsychiatric Nursing Approach to Intervention in a Problem of Mutual Withdrawal on a Mental Hospital Ward," *Psychiatry,* vol. 15, May, 1952, pp. 193–217.

Tumin, Melvin M., *Caste in a Peasant Society:* A Case Study in the Dynamics of Caste. Princeton University Press, Princeton, 1952. 300 pp.

"Some Fragments from the Life History of a Marginal Man," *Character and Personality,* vol. 13, March, 1945, pp. 261–296.

Tunis, Martin, and others, "Studies on Headache: Further Observations on Cranial and Conjunctival Vessels During and Between Vascular Headache Attacks," *Transactions* of the American Neurological Association, 1951, pp. 67–69.

Underwood, Frances W., and Irma Honigmann, "A Comparison of Socialization and Personality in Two Simple Societies," *American Anthropologist,* vol. 49, October-December, 1947, pp. 557–577.

Volkart, Edmund H., editor, *Social Behavior and Personality:* Contributions of W. I. Thomas to Theory and Social Research. Social Science Research Council, New York, 1951. 338 pp.

Wagley, Charles, *Amazon Town:* A Study of Man in the Tropics. Macmillan Co., New York, 1953. 305 pp. See especially "From Magic to Science," pp. 215–256.

Waller, Willard, *The Family:* A Dynamic Interpretation. 1938. 621 pp. Revised by Reuben L. Hill, Dryden Press, New York, 1951. 637 pp.

Warner, W. Lloyd, *A Black Civilization:* A Social Study of an Australian Tribe. Harper and Bros., New York, 1937. 594 pp.

American Life: Dream and Reality. University of Chicago Press, 1953. 268 pp.

"The Society, the Individual, and His Mental Disorders," *American Journal of Psychiatry,* vol. 94, September, 1937, pp. 275–284.

Warner, W. Lloyd, and Paul S. Lunt, *The Social Life of a Modern Community.* Yale University Press, New Haven, 1941. 460 pp.

WARNER, W. LLOYD, AND LEO SROLE, *The Social Systems of American Ethnic Groups*. Yale University Press, New Haven, 1945. 318 pp.

WARNER, W. LLOYD, AND OTHERS. *Social Class in America:* A Manual of Procedure for the Measurement of Social Status. Science Research Associates, Inc., Chicago, 1949. 274 pp.

WATERSON, ROLLEN, "Dichter Report: Doctor and Patient," *New York Medicine*, vol. 7, November, 20, 1951, pp. 16–22, 34–37.

WEINBERG, SAMUEL K., *Society and Personality Disorders*. Prentice-Hall, Inc., New York, 1952. 536 pp.

WEISS, EDWARD, AND O. S. ENGLISH, *Psychosomatic Medicine:* The Clinical Application of Psychopathology to General Medical Problems. 2d ed. W. B. Saunders Co., Philadelphia, 1949. 803 pp.

WELCH, LIVINGSTON, "Human Conditioning and Anxiety," *Annals* of the New York Academy of Sciences, vol. 56, February, 1953, pp. 266–276.

WESSEN, A. F., *The Social Structure of a Modern Hospital*. Department of Sociology, Yale University, 1950. Unpublished Ph.D. dissertation.

WEST, JAMES [CARL WITHERS], *Plainville, U.S.A.* Columbia University Press, New York, 1945. 238 pp.

WESTERMARCK, EDWARD A., *The Origin and Development of the Moral Ideas*. 2d ed. reprinted. Macmillan Co., New York, 1926. 2 vols.

WHEELER, WILLIAM M., *Social Life Among the Insects*. Harcourt, Brace and Co., New York, 1928. 375 pp.

WHITE, BENJAMIN V., AND OTHERS, *Mucous Colitis:* A Psychological Medical Study of Sixty Cases. *Psychosomatic Medicine*, Monograph I. National Research Council, Washington, 1939. 103 pp.

WHITE, LESLIE A., "History, Evolution, and Functionalism: Three Types of Interpretation of Culture," *Southwestern Journal of Anthropology*, vol. 1, Summer, 1945, pp. 221–248.

"Kroeber's Configurations of Culture Growth," *American Anthropologist*, vol. 48, January, 1946, pp. 78–93.

The Science of Culture: A Study of Man and Civilization. Farrar, Straus and Young, New York, 1949. 444 pp.

WHITE, PAUL D., "La Médecine du Coeur," *The Diplomate*, vol. 22, January, 1950, pp. 9–17.

White, William L., *Lost Boundaries.* Harcourt, Brace and Co., New York, 1948. 91 pp.

Whitehorn, John C., and others, editors, *Psychiatry and Medical Education:* Report of the Conference on Psychiatric Education at Cornell University, June 21–27, 1951. American Psychiatric Association, Washington, 1952. 164 pp. See especially "Human Ecology and Personality in the Training of Physicians," pp. 63–96.

Whiting, John W. H., *Becoming a Kwoma:* Teaching and Learning in a New Guinea Tribe. Yale University Press, New Haven, 1941. 226 pp.

Whyte, William F., *Street Corner Society:* The Structure of an Italian Slum. University of Chicago Press, 1943. 284 pp.

Williams, Robin M., Jr., *The Reduction of Intergroup Tensions.* Social Science Research Council, Bulletin 57, New York, 1947. 153 pp.

Winch, Robert F., "The Study of Personality in the Family Setting," *Social Forces,* vol. 28, March, 1950, pp. 310–316.

Wissler, Clark, *Man and Culture.* Edited by Seba Eldridge. Thomas Y. Crowell Co., New York, 1938. 365 pp.

Wofinden, R. C., "The Modern Trend in Social Medicine in the Home and in Industry," *Nursing Times,* vol. 46, June 24 and July 1, 1950, pp. 648–649, 674–675.

Wolf, G. A., Jr., and Harold G. Wolff, "Studies on the Nature of Certain Symptoms Associated with Cardiovascular Disorders," *Psychosomatic Medicine,* vol. 8, September–October, 1946, pp. 293–319.

Wolf, Stewart, and P. E. Messier, "Corneal Vascular Changes in Association with Conflict in a Patient with Phlyctenular Keratitis," *Proceedings* of the Association for Research in Nervous and Mental Disease, vol. 29, 1950, pp. 537–542.

Wolf, Stewart, and Harold G. Wolff, *Human Gastric Function:* An Experimental Study of a Man and His Stomach. 2d ed., rev. and enl. Oxford University Press, New York, 1947. 262 pp.

Wolff, Harold G., *Headache and Other Head Pain.* Oxford University Press, New York, 1948. 642 pp.

"Life Stress and Cardiovascular Disorders," *Circulation,* vol. 1, February, 1950, pp. 187–203.

"Protective Reaction Patterns and Disease," *Annals of Internal Medicine,* vol. 27, December, 1947, pp. 944–969.

Wolff, Harold G., *Stress and Disease*. Charles C. Thomas, Springfield, Ill., 1953. 199 pp. See especially "Experimentally Observed Effects of Stress in Man," pp. 44–144; and "The Patient-Physician Relationship and the Alteration of Attitudes and Bodily Reactions," pp. 145–147.

Wolff, Harold G., Stewart Wolf, and others, "Changes in Form and Function of the Mucous Membranes Occurring as Part of Protective Reaction Patterns in Man During Periods of Life Stress and Emotional Conflict," *Transactions* of the Association of American Physicians, vol. 61, 1948, pp. 313–334.

Wollenberger, A., and M. A. Linton, Jr., "The Metabolism of Glucose in Starvation and Water Deprivation," *American Journal of Physiology*, vol. 148, March, 1947, pp. 597–609.

Woodard, James W., "The Relation of Personality Structure to the Structure of Culture," *American Sociological Review*, vol. 3, October, 1938, pp. 637–651.

Yawger, N. S., "Emotions as the Cause of Rapid and Sudden Death," *Archives of Neurology and Psychiatry*, vol. 36, October, 1936, pp. 875–879.

Yerkes, Robert M., *Chimpanzees:* A Laboratory Colony. Yale University Press, New Haven, 1943. 321 pp.

Yerkes, Robert M., and A. W. Yerkes, "Social Behavior in Infrahuman Primates" in *A Handbook of Social Psychology*, edited by Carl A. Murchison, 1935, pp. 973–1033.

Young, Paul T., *Emotion in Man and Animal:* Its Nature and Relation to Attitude and Motive. John Wiley and Sons, New York, 1943. 422 pp.

Zilboorg, Gregory, "Masculine and Feminine: Some Biological and Cultural Aspects," *Psychiatry*, vol. 7, August, 1944, pp. 257–296.

Mind, Medicine, and Man. Harcourt, Brace and Co., New York, 1943. 344 pp.

Zilboorg, Gregory, and G. W. Henry, *A History of Medical Psychology*. W. W. Norton and Co., New York, 1941. 606 pp.

Zimmerman, Carl C., *Family and Civilization*. Harper and Bros., New York, 1947. 829 pp.

Zuckerman, Solly, *The Social Life of Monkeys and Apes*. Harcourt, Brace and Co., New York, 1932. 375 pp.

Index

Index